EXPERIMENTATION
WITH
MICROPROCESSOR
APPLICATIONS

EXPERIMENTATION WITH MICROPROCESSOR APPLICATIONS

THOMAS W. DAVIS, P. E.
CHAIRMAN, ELECTRICAL ENGINEERING
DEPARTMENT
MILWAUKEE SCHOOL OF ENGINEERING

RESTON PUBLISHING COMPANY, INC.
A Prentice-Hall Company
Reston, Virginia

Library of Congress Cataloging in Publication Data

Davis, Thomas W
  Experimentation with microprocessor applications.

  1. Microprocessors -- Laboratory manuals.
I. Title
QA76.5.D295   001.64'04'028   80-24272
ISBN 0-8359-1812-2

© 1981 by Reston Publishing Co., Inc.
A Prentice-Hall Company
Reston, Virginia 22090

10 9 8 7 6 5 4 3 2 1

Printed in the United States

Preface

The necessity for developing programs in microprocessor education is obvious. However, the manner in which these programs are structured and the merit of the laboratory sessions have a great influence on their overall worth. Microprocessor applications must be integrated into existing programs to give the students practical illustrations of otherwise academic topics. As most course descriptions say, "laboratory sessions will reinforce the lecture topics". The laboratory provides the opportunity to bring together all of the material of the lecture sessions. Practically oriented experiments provide a motivational factor necessary for the students to, in effect, teach themselves. Experiments of the type dealt with in this manual tend to develop independent thought often resulting in a greater desire to further pursue the topic.

This manual has been designed to be used in conjunction with any of the textbooks presently on the market, but could also be used as a guide for the self-motivating student to learn more about microprocessor applications. It is recommended that the student concentrate on a specific microprocessor/microcomputer and use this system throughout all of the experiments, thereby lessening the change for confusion. Upon completion of this program of study, the student will be better able to generalize from the specifics learned and work with other systems.

Each experiment is intended to emphasize a specific topic area such as instructions, interfacing, or algorithm development. The experiments follow a general pattern:

1. statement of the problem,

2. background information,

3. a general outline of the procedure.

More detail is provided in some experiments than in others. Some even have open-ended design problems that will allow the creativeness and innovativeness of the student to become evident. Due to the abundance of experiments, this manual may be used in one, two or three separate courses, or different experiments may be used on an alternating semester basis.

In addition to the normal microcomputer configuration (RAM, I/O ports and support chips), the only other equipment required would be commonly available TTL integrated circuits and an A/D and D/A converter, 7 segment displays and a keyboard. The experiments have been structured such that equipment substitutions can be easily made.

In the closing paragraphs of a preface, it is often appropriate to thank those people who have contributed to the writing of a book and this will be no exception. I wish to thank all of my students who have labored on less refined versions of these experiments and a special thank you to Ann Uriell who has labored to help me make these experiments more refined.

June 1980   T. W. Davis

Table of Contents

EXPERIMENTATION WITH MICROPROCESSOR APPLICATIONS

Experiment 1

HISTORY OF COMPUTERS AND MICROPROCESSORS

Purpose

The purpose of this experiment is to gain greater insight into and appreciation for the microprocessor and its historical development. In addition, a search of available literature will be required.

Background Investigation

The entire process which eventually led to the present state-of-the-art began back somewhere between 100 BC and 1300 AD with the introduction and wide spread use of the Abacus. Although this device represented a great improvement over pebble counting, it required centuries for it to come into general use. Subsequent events occurred within a far greater compression of time.

Probably the most widely recognized "computer" was designed in 1833 by Charles Babbage. His analytical engine was a maze of gears and mechanical components driven by steam power. It had a memory of 50,000 digits and could follow programmed instructions. The whole idea was considered to be so ridiculous by most people, that the machine was never built.

The first true data processing computer was built and put into use by Herman Hollerith to tabulate the 1870 census. The machine reduced what would have normally taken 20 years to complete to only three years.

In 1937, George Stibitz built a binary adder on his kitchen table from bulbs, flashlight batteries, relays and switches. This was the first application of binary arithmetic and electric logic to mathematical computations. George Stibitz continued to develop additional hardware.

In 1944, after seven years of development, the first large-scale automatic digital computer was completed. The automatic sequence controlled calculator was developed by Howard Aiken and could add and subtract in 3/10 of a second, multiply in 6 seconds and divide in 16 seconds.

The ENIAC, the first electronic digital computer, occupied a space

1

of 1500 square feet, weighed 30 tons and contained over 18,000 vacuum tubes and 500,000 switches and was developed in 1946. It required 130,000 watts to operate and could perform 5000 additions or 300 multiplications per second.

In 1950, there were only 60 computers in operation. One of these machines was built by the National Bureau of Standards. The SSEC computer of the same era solved an atomic energy problem that involved 9,000,000 mathematical operations in 150 hours. It would have taken a mathematician 1500 years to solve the same problem by hand.

It was estimated in 1954 that 50 companies could eventually use computers in their work. The UNIVAC I and the IBM 701 were introduced near this time.

NCR introduced the first all transistorized computer. The CPU had 8000 diodes and 4000 transistors and a total of 4800 words of storage. IBM introduced the concept of the computer family in 1964 with the 360 series machines. These third generation computers were smaller and faster than ever before because of the miniaturization revolution in electronics.

The minicomputer industry can trace its origin back to the mid-sixties. Digital Equipment Corporation is generally recognized with developing the minicomputer in the form we see it today. By 1971, there were over 100,000 computers in use world wide.

In 1971, Intel developed and introduced the first widely accepted microprocessor. This device was equivalent to a central processing unit and entirely contained on a single integrated circuit approximately 100 mils square. It consumed only 450 milliwatts of power and can execute over 46 different instructions, most in microseconds.

Further investigation into the microprocessor development will be left to the experimental portion of this section. Many interesting facts regarding the history of these devices may be uncovered which will lead to a broader understanding of this important topical area.

Prelaboratory Investigation

For each of the questions given below, determine the most appropriate answer relating all facts regarding the microprocess/microcomputer evolution.

1. Who developed the first microprocessor? In what year?

2. Which microprocessor was considered to be the most widely accepted?

3. The first eight bit microprocessor was developed by _____ in _____ (year).

4. Which company introduced the 16 bit microprocessor?

5. Draw a chart depicting the evolution of the major components that make computer systems possible (relays, tubes, etc.).

6. Which manufacturers, and specifically which device, first introduced a microprocessor to conform to military specifications?

7. What is the highest density semiconductor memory available on a single integrated circuit?

8. Which electronic game was first introduced that contained a microprocessor?

9. Develop a chart showing the decline in cost of an 8 bit microprocessor from inception to the present.

10. How many 8 bit microprocessors are currently manufactured and by whom? 16 bit?

11. Who first introduced the home computer and what was its basic cost?

12. What individual(s) were credited with the development of the microprocessor?

13. What is the distinct difference between a minicomputer and a microcomputer?

14. What factors have lead to the wide acceptance of the microprocessor?

15. Can a distinction still be drawn between a microprocessor and a microcomputer? Will this always be true?

16. What can be projected for the future microprocessor/microcomputer field?

Laboratory Investigation

Time should be set aside during a laboratory period to discuss the findings of the prelaboratory investigation. General discussion of related facts that were uncovered during the research would be appropriate.

Questions for Further Study

1. Write a short narrative summary outlining the major discoveries dealing with the microprocessor.

2. Draw a chronological flow diagram outlining the major breakthroughs in microprocessor/microcomputer technology.

Experiment 2

Purpose

The purpose of this experiment is to become familiar with the basic instruction set, addressing modes and condition flags.

Background Investigation

The actual number of different instructions for a microprocessor may vary from 40 to over 250. The problem of managing such a large set may seem overwhelming at first but when the set is broken down into basic groups, it becomes more manageable and even easy to remember. The large number of instructions are a result of several variations of each of the basic instructions.

The first portion of an instruction that determines the operation to be performed is called the OP code or operation code. In the standard 8 bit processor, one whole word is reserved for this purpose. This results in 256 different possible combinations. However, some of these are usually unassigned or not used. Larger word length microprocessors, such as 16 bits may use a portion of the word for addressing assignments, indexing or special operations. The remaining words, or bytes in an eight bit processor instruction specify an operand, an address or information from which an address is obtained during execution.

The computer can only execute instructions which are represented in binary form. This binary representation is called machine code. An alpha representation of the machine code, usually consisting of one to five letters, is most often used to represent an instruction and tend to make the program more readable. Programs which convert these mnemonics into the binary machine language are called assemblers and will be covered in a later experiment. Most references made to instructions here will be the mnemonic representation. It is a simple process to convert this to binary representation usually expressed in octal or hexidecimal notation. It is convenient to develop a chart to perform this conversion and use it when doing assembly without the aid of an assembler program.

Instructions can basically be divided into major groups or divisions. These include:

Data Transfer. Moving data to or from memory, transfer of data within the processor such as accumulator to accumulator or accumulator to temporary register and input/output.

Arithmetic. Addition, subtraction, increment, decrement, add with carry, negate, compare, and even multiply and divide on some processors.

Logical. AND, OR, complement, rotate, exclusive OR, etc.

Branch Group. Conditional and unconditional jump or branch instructions, subroutine calls, returns and interrupt instructions.

Stack Operations. Push, pop or pull and loading the stack pointer.

Machine Control. Including instructions such as halt, wait and wait for interrupt.

Memory for the microprocessor is organized such that each word has a unique address. The address of data and instructions use the same format. Often, the desired location may be referenced using more than one procedure depending on the addressing modes of the processor. Modes of addressing may be classified as listed below. Although all may not be available on each processor, all will have multiple addressing methods.

Direct - In this case, the second or second and third words of the instruction contain the exact memory address of the data or location to be executed.

Immediate - The second or second and third words contain the data itself. The instruction contains not only the operation but also the data to be operated upon (the operand).

Indirect - A register or instruction may contain a pointer address. The pointer address is the location where the exact or absolute address is stored.

Inherent or Register - The instruction's OP code specifies the location of the data. Instructions of this type are usually only one word in length.

Indexed - Addresses are specified relative to a special index register which contains an entire address specification.

Relative - Addresses may be specified relative to the current location of program execution (the contents of the program counter). Specific rules may limit the distance in either direction relative to the present value of the program counter.

Memory reference instructions that perform the same operations may use one or more of the modes listed above. This is one of the factors which account for the large number of instructions.

Condition codes (sometimes called condition flags or processor status words) are also an important consideration when investigating the operation of instructions. They become the prime influence in the decision making process in a microprocessor system. Not all instructions affect the condition of these flags. Such instructions as COMPARE, ADD, AND, OR, etc., are used to set the proper codes so that branch and jump instructions are properly executed.

The condition codes given below are a representative sample of the ones found in most microprocessor systems.

Zero - If, as the result of an instruction, the accumulator goes to zero, this flag will be set.

Sign (also called negative) - This bit is the same as the most significant bit in the accumulator. It should be remembered, however, that it is changed only following certain instructions.

Carry (also called borrow) - If an instruction resulted in an overflow from addition or borrow from subtracting, this flag is set. It may also be changed due to a rotate right or left instruction. (This can be used to check the condition of individual bits within a data word.

Auxiliary Carry (also called half carry) - If the instruction causes a carry from the bit 3 to bit 4, this flag is set. It is normally used in decimal adjust accumulator instructions.

Parity - If even parity (Mod 2 sum of the bits equal 0) results from an instruction, this flag is set. If odd parity, flag is reset.

Additional conditions within the processor may be included as part of the processor status word. These include twos complement overflow, interrupt status, etc.

Prelaboratory Investigation

1. Classify each of the instructions available in the microprocessor according to those outlined above.

2. Determine the various addressing modes available for your specific microprocessor.

3. Develop or obtain a quick reference guide for the machine language coding of the instructions.

4. Classify each of the rotate instructions as to their operation with respect to the carry or overflow bit.

5. List as many ways as possible that can be used to load data into the accumulator.

6. It is desired to branch to a given address if bit 2 in the accumulator (bit 0 is the LSB) is set to 1. List at least two different procedures to accomplish this.

7. Classify the instructions as to one word, two word, and three word instructions.

8. List the different ways data may be placed into memory.

9. Which instructions will affect the contents of the stack?

10. What is the basic difference between a jump or branch instruction and a call subroutine instruction?

11. How would it be possible to set all condition codes to zero at the same time?

12. List at least four instructions that will modify the stack pointer.

13. For each of the specified operations listed below, devise an instruction or group of instructions to accomplish the task.

   a) Clear the accumulator.

   b) Determine the negative (twos complement) of a number in the accumulator.

   c) Clear the carry or overflow bit.

   d) Set all bits in the accumulator to zero except bit 4.

   e) Initialize the stack pointer at a specific address and place the contents of the accumulator on the stack.

   f) Add one to a given memory location.

   g) Address a group of sequential memory locations and move this data, one word at a time, to the accumulator.

   h) Set the accumulator to 2 using only three instructions or less.

   i) Give two ways to multiply the contents of the accumulator by 2.

   j) Duplicate two memory locations and store them at a different address.

14. Write a short program which will add two numbers stored in memory and place the result back in memory.

15. Write a program to search successive memory locations until a $F4_H$ is found.

Laboratory Investigation

1. Become familiar with the method used to enter programs for your particular microprocessor system.

2. Devise a procedure whereby the contents of the accumulator and the carry bit may be easily displayed.

3. Test each portion of step 13 in the prelaboratory investigation.

4. Verify the correct operation of the program in step 14 of the prelaboratory investigation.

5. Test the correct operation of the program of step 15 in the prelaboratory investigation.

Questions for Further Study

1. Define the term microprogramming.

2. What is the difference between machine and assembly language programming?

3. How would it be possible to display the condition codes?

4. Draw a map of all the available memory space for your system. Show which addresses are occupied by RAM, PROM, I/O, etc.

5. Draw an operational flowchart depicting the correct procedure for entering machine language programs.

6. Explain the terms:

   Compiler

   Interpreter

   Translator

   and how they relate to computer software.

Experiment 3

INSTRUCTION TIMING

Purpose

The various aspects of clocks, instruction timing and delay loops will be discussed in this experiment.

Background Investigation

Proper executing of instructions and the subsequent programs they form requires that the specific operations be performed in a predetermined sequence. This sequencing is accomplished by timing circuits found in the control unit. The time base used for this sequencing is supplied by some sort of external source. The crystal or R/C network used in conjunction with the time base is used to determine the frequency of the timing pulses. A crystal is most often used because the precise time of execution for each instruction must be known if software delays are employed in a programming application.

Depending on the processor used, the frequency of oscillation may be from 1 MHz to 8 MHz. Actually, the sequencing pulses are derived from the base frequency and do not affect the order of operation but only the speed with which they are executed. The upper limit for the clock frequency can be found in the manufacturers' specifications. These specifications usually define a maximum frequency, time between pulses and pulse width for processors where the timing source is external. These components comprise what is called the master clock. For the Intel 8080 for example, a two phase, non-overlapping clock is required. Minimum and maximum values are specified for clock period, rise and fall time, pulse width (for both ϕ_1 and ϕ_2), time between ϕ_1 and ϕ_2 as well as time between leading edges of ϕ_1 and ϕ_2. Various integrated circuit master clock chips are available which will generate the appropriate signals. With other processors, this may be found on the processor chip itself.

Each manufacturer has a unique method for the decomposition of each instruction cycle (the total time required to execute an instruction). Each instruction cycle may be broken down into various machine cycles that are each composed of a number of cycles of the master clock. These may all be a variable length depending upon the number of operations to be performed for each individual instruction. The three major machine cycles that can be found on most systems are

FETCH, DEFER and EXECUTE.

During the FETCH cycle, an OP code is obtained from memory. The OP code is decoded in the instruction decoder portion of the control unit. Once the processor knows the type of instruction to be executed, the length and number of the remaining machine cycles may be determined. The remaining bytes are then obtained from memory.

If the instruction contains additional address information in subsequent bytes, a DEFER cycle may be entered. In this case, addresses for the data may be obtained from memory. When indirect addressing is employed, the pointer address will be used to obtain the final addressing information.

The EXECUTE cycle is the final cycle of operation where the operand is obtained from memory and the operations on the data are performed. These would include ADD, OR, SUBTRACT, etc.

Obviously, not all instructions would require that the processor execute each machine cycle. A jump instruction may not require a DEFER or EXECUTE cycle because all of the required information necessary to modify the instruction may be obtained during the fetch cycle. The following series of operations are typical for the instruction cycle for an indirect ADD.

Clock Cycle	Operation	Machine Cycle
1	Send contents of program counter to memory	FETCH
2	Obtain OP code from memory (ADD indirect)	FETCH
3	Decode operation	FETCH
4	Set up remaining timing, obtain pointer address information	FETCH
5	Employ pointer address to obtain data address	DEFER
6	Send data address to memory	DEFER
7	Obtain data from memory (load into temporary register)	EXECUTE
8	Add with contents of accumulator	EXECUTE
9	Place result in accumulator and set appropriate flags	EXECUTE

The timing diagram below shows the relationship between the various timing signals and clock signals. In this hypothetical example, a total of nine clock cycles are used to execute this instruction. (Note: In systems with a two phase clock, timing is referenced with respect to one phase only.) If the fundamental clock frequency for this example was 2 Mhz (crystal controlled), then the total execution time would be 4.5 µsec.

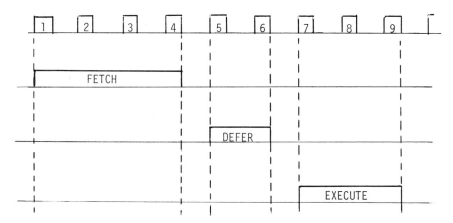

Figure 1: Instruction Cycle

Each of the instructions in the set has a specified number of clock cycles required for execution. Therefore, the precise time for execution may be determined. A few of these may have two execution times listed such as in the case of a conditional jump or branch instruction. The longer time is specified if the branch is true and the shorter time if it is false.

The knowledge of the execution time coupled with a crystal controlled clock can produce precise timing loops that may be used for program delay, precision output timing and a variety of other programming applications. In fact a subroutine may be developed to provide a specified delay for use in later programs.

When writing timing programs, the no-operation instruction (NOP) is often used to "fine tune" the delay period and produce the specified delay. Even though no operation is performed with this instruction, it does take time to execute. In addition NOP instructions are frequently used in machine language programming to reserve space for forgotten instructions.

A simple delay routine is shown in the flowchart in figure 2. The program is written as a subroutine and the instruction execution

11

times are shown simply as t_1, t_2..., etc., at the right of each block. The internal looping routine provides the majority of the delay time. It has been assumed that the counter, N, contains the length of the delay routine. It can be shown that the total delay time is:

$$T_D = t_1+(t_2+t_3+t_4+t_5)N+t_6$$

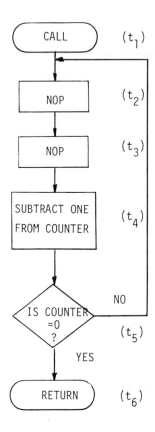

Figure 2: Simple Delay Routine

The NOP instructions are used to provide an additional delay necessary to increase the overall time. t_1 and t_6 are fixed and do not become part of the looping process. The shortest delay obtainable with this program is with N=1 and would be $t_1+t_2+t_3+t_4+t_5+t_6$. The longest delay would depend on the maximum size for N (usually one word length). This formula may also be used to calculate the value of N necessary to produce a desired delay. Because t_n and T_D are known,

12

then

$$N = \frac{T_D - t_1 - t_6}{(t_2 + t_3 + t_4 + t_5)}$$

Additional NOP instructions may be added within the loop to significantly increase the time needed for delay (Nt_{NOP}) or outside the loop
to fine tune the time. It should be pointed out that if this routine
is to be reused, the counter N must be reset to its initial value before each CALL.

A double nested timing loop is shown in the flowchart of figure
3. The time delay is significantly lengthened by this process.

$$T_D = t_1 + ((t_2 + t_3 + t_4)N_1 + t_5 + t_6 + t_7)N_2 + t_8$$

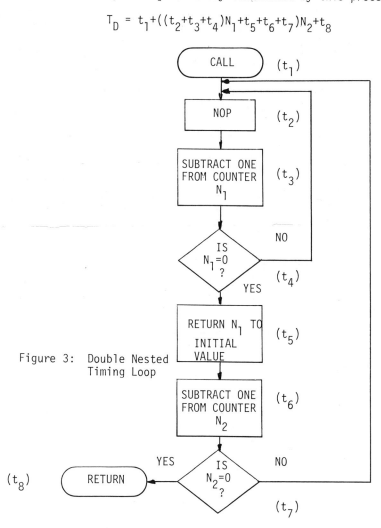

Figure 3: Double Nested
Timing Loop

13

Delay times from a few microseconds to several milliseconds may be obtained from a single loop delay. A two loop program can result in delays of several seconds. Delays of several hours are possible without using a large amount of memory. The importance of using these delay routines will be evident in the next examples. In fact, some processors even have a built-in DELAY instruction.

Speech synthesis on the computer has long intrigued many people. There are current devices on the market that will generate sound recognizable as human speech. They are used in calculators for the blind, chess games and are even available on some home computer systems. They use information stored in memory to time an output signal that simply switches a bit on and off. Other systems may play prerecorded messages on a tape that is selected by the computer system.

As a way of introduction to this speech synthesis area and to aid in familiarization with instruction timing, an investigation of tone generation will be made. Although the computer cannot easily generate a sine wave, it can generate a square wave by simply turning one of the output bits on or off at the proper frequency.

The ON-OFF action of the accumulator can be accomplished by successive increments. Because the remaining bits are of no concern, the accumulator contents can effectively count from 0 to 255_{10}. This will cause the least significant bit to "oscillate" between 0 and 1. A delay routine can set the ON period and OFF period. It is also assumed that the output port contains a latch so the output data will change only when it is written over.

A flowchart showing this procedure is given in figure 4. The delay time may be calculated using the procedure previously discussed.

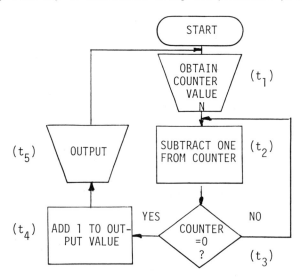

Figure 4: Tone Generation Routine

14

The delay time may be determined to be:

$$T_D = (t_2+t_3)N+(t_1+t_4+t_5)$$

This is the time the pulse is either on or off. The total period of the waveform is therefore $(T_D) \times 2$ due to the fact that the loop is symmetrical. The times $t_1,t_2,t_3...$ are based on the clock frequency of the microprocessor. Using these relationships, the output tone frequency will be given by:

$$f = \frac{1}{2(T_D)}$$

The frequency for the tone generated may be determined from the table listed below.

NOTE	FREQUENCY
C	261.63
D	293.66
E	329.63
F	349.23
G	392.00 (196, Low Octave)
A	440.00
B	493.88

Using a second delay loop to determine the length of time each note is to be played, it is possible to store the delay lengths in memory, thus creating a tune. It should be pointed out that the other octaves of the notes given above may be found by simply multiplying or dividing the frequencies by 2.

Various methods are available for the monitoring of the output waveform. In some cases, a speaker may be simply connected to the output bit. A capacitor may be used to insure that if the program were stopped while the output was at a logical 1, then the speaker would not appear as a short to ground.

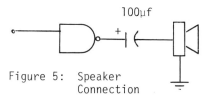

100µf

Figure 5: Speaker
          Connection

An LM 380 audio power amplifier may also be employed to drive a speaker for the tone generation system. Figure 6 shows its connection.

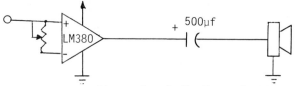

Figure 6: Audio Power Amplifier

Two outputs may be handled by either of the two connections shown in figure 7. These may be used to generate two simultaneous tones.

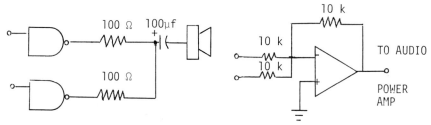

Figure 7: Two Tone Generation

Prelaboratory Investigation

1. Code the single loop delay routine, as previously discussed, as a subroutine. It should provide an input for an adjustable delay as prescribed at the time of call.

2. Repeat step 1 above for the two loop delay routine.

3. For the delay routines (one and two loop), calculate, using the clock frequency of your microcomputer unit, the minimum and maximum delay times.

4. Using the tone generation scheme previously discussed, write a program to generate the musical scale.

5. The Westminster Chimes are familiar to most people. Program the processor to "play" this tune. (Hint: The notes required are E, C, D, G (low octave), G, D, E, C.)

6. In the tone generation programs, is it important to know what the value of the accumulator is initially?

Laboratory Investigation

1. Experimentally determine the minimum and maximum delay times for the single loop routine written in step 1 of the prelaboratory investigation.

2. Repeat step 1 above for the two loop delay routine.

3. Using an oscilloscope or frequency counter, verify the correct frequency generated for each note of the musical scale.

4. Because the accumulator is incremented after each timing loop in the program of figure 4, determine the relationship between the data bits d_0 to d_7.

Questions for Further Study

1. The tones generated for use in conjunction with the telephone are actually a sum of two distinct tones. Decompose these two frequencies using a filter and a frequency counter. (Hint: Each row has its own frequency and each column has its own. Each key is a sum of these two frequencies.)

2. Using the data from step 1 above, generate these tones using the programs from this experiment.

3. Write a short program to generate the word HELLO using the tone generation and delay routines from this experiment.

4. How may the output signal be modified to produce a sine wave output?

Experiment 9

BINARY ADDITION AND SUBTRACTION

Purpose

The intent of this experiment is to provide some familiarity with binary numbers, two's complement notation, addition and subtraction.

Background

The use of positional notation for the representation of numbers is not unfamiliar and is often employed for the conversion of most bases to base 10. In fact, the base 10 system employs this positional notation.

$$546_{10} = 5 \times 10^2 + 4 \times 10^1 + 6 \times 10^0$$

The binary system,

$$10111_2 = 1 \times 2^4 + 0 \times 2^3 + 1 \times 2^2 + 1 \times 2^1 + 1 \times 2^0 = 23_{10}$$

the octal system,

$$374_8 = 3 \times 8^2 + 7 \times 8^1 + 4 \times 8^0 = 252_{10}$$

and the hexidecimal system,

$$10FD_{16} = 1 \times 16^3 + 0 \times 10^2 + 15 \times 16^1 + 13 \times 16^0 = 4349_{10}$$

all use this form of positional notation.

Binary addition follows basically the same set of rules as base 10 addition. There is however one special case:

$$0+0 = 0$$

$$1+0 = 1$$

$$0+1 = 1$$

$$1+1 = \underline{10} \quad \text{(special case)}$$

The carry, underlined, represents the special case where an answer of 2 is not allowed. The addition of large binary numbers is an easy task recalling the same rules as employed in based 10.

$$10011101$$

$$+ \underline{01011011}$$

$$11111000$$

The logic circuitry necessary to accomplish this is not too complex and is found on all microprocessor systems. The basic set of rules is implemented into a device called a half adder. When the possibility of a carry into the next higher position exists, such as the example above, a full adder is employed. Eight full adders can be used to add two eight bit words in a computer system.

The range of possible base ten values that can be represented in a single eight bit number is 0 to 255_{10} provided that negative numbers are excluded. When signed binary numbers are used, one bit position is reserved to indicate the sign. The most significant bit position is used and 0 indicates a positive value and 1 indicates a negative value. Using this convention, it is well to remember that zero is considered to be a positive number by the system.

The logic circuitry needed to perform a subtraction (or the addition of a positive number and a negative number) can be constructed in a similar fashion as the adder logic, namely, using a half subtractor and a full subtractor. Instead of the carry terminology however a borrow term is used. In systems that perform subtraction as well as addition, the extra circuitry needed to do both operations would add considerable extra cost. A method for the representation of negative binary numbers exists which will allow adder circuitry to perform subtraction. The representation is called complement notation.

One's complement of a number may be found by converting all of the ones to zeros and all the zeros to ones. Using an eight bit word length, an example is given below:

$$56_{10} = 00111000_{2}$$

$$- 56_{10} = 11000111_{2} \text{ (ones notation)}$$

Note the most significant bit (MSB) is now a one and therefore representative of a negative value. Using this notation it is now a simple manner to perform subtraction. With this procedure, however, the carry out of the high order bit is added back into the answer to form the correct result. It is referred to as an end around carry.

Decimal Subtraction	Binary Subtraction	One's Complement Addition
62	00111110	00111110
- 56		+ 11000111
6		1 00000101

end around
carry

00000110

In the following example the end around carry is zero indicating
that the answer is negative. It is already in one's complement form.
To find the absolute value of the answer, all that is necessary is
to recomplement. Recomplementing may be performed by exactly the
same procedure as complementing.

56	00111000	00111000
- 62	- 00111110	+ 11000001
		0 11111001

No end around carry indicators
as negative result.

$$|-6| = |11111001| = 00000110 = 6_{10}$$

In many systems, negative values are stored in their complemented
form.

Due to the step involved in the addition process by adding the
end around carry, an alternate complementing process using the two's
complement method is most often used. Actually the two's complement
is the one's complement plus one. The end around carry is simply performed when the complement is done and not after the addition process.

$$-56 = -(00111000)$$

11000111

+ 1

11001000   (two's complement form)

Two's complement notation is widely used in computer systems to store
negative numbers and the addition circuitry assumes two's complement
subtraction (because it ignors the end around carry).

It may be advisable to further investigate the characteristics of two's complement notation before studying subtraction using this notation. Recall that the MSB of the accumulator is the sign bit and that the inverse complement may be formed by exactly the same procedure as the complement.

It can therefore be shown that the value

$$11111111$$

is a negative number and its absolute value can be found by:

$$11111111$$

$$00000000 \quad \text{(one's complement)}$$

$$\underline{\qquad +1}$$

$$00000001$$

and is therefore representative of -1_{10}. Similarly -2_{10} can be represented by:

$$11111110$$

and -127_{10} by:

$$10000001$$

and -128_{10} by:

$$10000000.$$

Note that in the above case, recomplementing the value yields the same value hence,

$$|10000000| = 10000000 = -128_{10}$$

In these cases, it can be shown that the range of values for an eight bit number is:

$$-128_{10} \leq V \leq 127_{10}$$

including zero gives the 256 possible combinations.

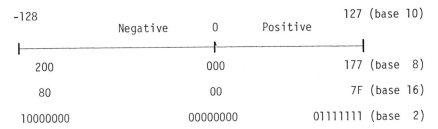

Figure 1: Range of an Eight Bit Signed Number

Subtraction using two's complement notation can be performed by using the rules of addition as in the following example.

Decimal Subtraction	Binary Subtraction	Two's Complement Addition
62	00111110	00111110
- 42	- 00101010	+ 11010110
20		1 00010100

Carry out is ignored.

Special considerations must be imposed when adding or subtracting numbers close to the maximum and minimum ranges. It is possible, for example, to add two positive numbers and get a negative due to overflow conditions. The carry flags must be closely monitored if the range of numbers is not known. This monitoring will insure that double precision will be employed where necessary.

The following examples will illustrate the cases which may be encountered in binary arithmetic operations.

Hex Notation	Binary Notation	Two's Complement Notation
Case 1:		
6F	0110 1111	0110 1111
- 2F	- (0010 1111)	+ 1101 0001
40		1 0100 0000

Carry out is ignored.

Case 2:

6F	0110 1111	0110 1111
- 70	- (0111 0000)	+ 1001 0000
- 01		[0] 1111 1111

Carry term 0, answer -1.

Note: As long as the two numbers are of opposite sign, an overflow condition cannot exist.

Case 3:

6F	0110 1111	0110 1111
- (-D1)	- (1111 1111)	+ 0000 0001
70		[0] 0111 1111

No carry.

Case 4:

6F	0110 1111	0110 1111
- (-70)	- (1001 0000)	+ 0111 0000
DF		[0] 1101 1111

No carry. Result appears negative. Overflow exists.

Case 5:

-05_H	1111 1010	1111 1011
- $(-70)_H$	- (1001 0000)	+ 0111 0000
$+6A_H$		[1] 0110 1011

Carry term.

Case 6:

-70_H	1001 0000	1001 0000
- (-05_H)	- (1111 1010)	+ 0000 0101
$-6C_H$		[0] 1001 0101

No carry term.

23

Case 7:

$$-70_H \qquad\qquad 1001\ 0000 \qquad\qquad\qquad 1001\ 0000$$
$$-\ (+5_H) \qquad\quad -\ (0000\ 0101) \qquad\qquad +\ 1111\ 1011$$

$$\qquad\qquad\qquad\qquad\qquad\qquad\qquad\qquad \boxed{1}\quad 1000\ 1011$$

$$-75_H$$

Carry term.

Case 8:

$$-40_H \qquad\qquad 1100\ 0000 \qquad\qquad\qquad 1100\ 0000$$
$$-(70_H) \qquad\quad -\ (0111\ 0000) \qquad\qquad +\ 1001\ 0000$$

$$\qquad\qquad\qquad\qquad\qquad\qquad\qquad\qquad \boxed{1}\quad 0101\ 0000$$

$$-B\emptyset_H$$

Carry term. Result appears
 positive. Overflow exists.

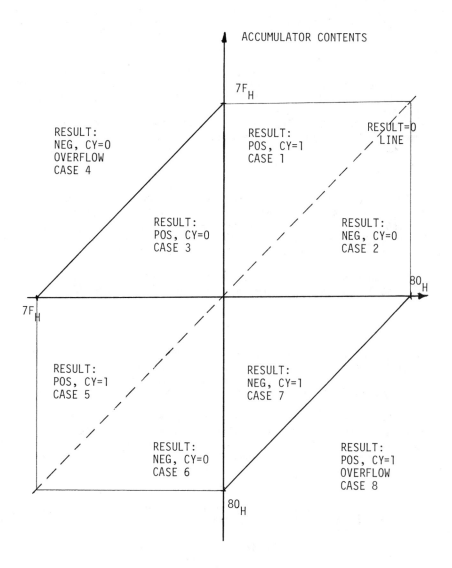

Figure 2: Summary of the Result of Subtracting
a Register r from the Contents of the
Accumulator

The graph shown in figure 2 is a summary of the result of performing a subtraction of two binary numbers, A and r where A is the contents of the accumulator and r represents the contents of some other memory location or another accumulator. This graph can also be used to determine the result of an instruction such as COMPARE. The only difference between COMPARE and SUBTRACT is that the results are not saved and only the flags are set.

When an overflow does exist, additional memory locations may be used to extend the precision of the answer. Such instructions as ADD with CARRY or SUBTRACT with BORROW are employed. Some processors have instructions which are strictly intended for double precision operations. An instruction such as double precision add is not uncommon. Using a signed double precision number, the range of values would be:

$$-32,768 \leq V \leq 32,767$$

Many processors have software which can perform operations on floating point numbers as well as the fixed point numbers previously discussed. Routines for performing addition and subtraction are, however, considerably more difficult. A brief look into their storage format may provide some insight for their further study.

Many possible formats exist for storing floating point numbers. Their base 10 counterparts are, however, usually expressed in the same form:

$$\pm.NNNN \times 10^{\pm NN}$$

This is a similar form to scientific notation without numbers to the left of the decimal point. Two signs are included, one for the mantissa and one for the exponent. Various formatting rules, such as those found in Fortran, allow the numbers to be printed in any format.

Binary representation of the floating point numbers requires the use of two or more words, particularly when the word length is eight bits. Depending on the precision involved and the range of values of the exponent, longer word lengths may be advantageous such as 16 bits. Minicomputers may use floating point numbers composed of 16, 24, 32 or even 48 bits.

A typical storage method may be devised based on three 8-bit words. This 24-bit form would appear as:

XXXXXXXX	Word #1
↑	
(sign of mantissa)	
XXXXXXXX	Word #2

XXXXXXXX   Word #3
‿‿‿‿‿‿‿
        Exponent
    ↑
    (sign of exponent)

     In the sample format shown, the mantissa is comprised of a
17 bit signed number and therefore its range would be:

$$-.65536 \leq N \leq +.65535$$

The exponent is a signed seven bit quantity and would have the range
of:

$$-64 \leq E \leq +63$$

This type of floating point format would, in reality, only yield
4 digits of significance.

     When investigating a higher level language, the restrictions
placed on the base 10 numbers always provide a clue as to their
binary storage scheme. For example, one BASIC software package gives
the following specifications:

     Integer values ±32,767

     Floating point numbers 6 significant digits in the
     range 10^{63} to 10^{-63}.

     If the processor employs a 16 bit word, it can be safely assumed
that integer values are stored in a single word while floating point
values require multiple words. A further investigation of floating
point arithmetic will be left to a more advanced discussion of higher
level languages.

Prelaboratory Investigation

1. A quantity used in many systems to check errors in the transfer of
    large amounts of data is called a checksum. It is simply the
    sum, without regard to sign or carry terms, of all the data.
    When data is transferred along with the appropriate checksum, the
    transferring program can keep its own checksum to provide an
    error detection scheme when the transfer is complete. Write
    a short program which will find the checksum of the data between
    any two specified addresses in memory.

2. Write a short routine to check for overflow based on the initial
    signs of the numbers to be subtracted and the resulting carry bit.

3. Write a routine which will produce a double precision result if
    the accumulator overflows due to the addition of two numbers.

27

4. Assume two double precision integer numbers are stored in memory. Write a routine which will add them together.

5. Repeat step 4 for the subtraction of the two double precision numbers.

6. What is the simplest way to determine the complement of a number?

Laboratory Investigation

1. Investigate the addition of two binary numbers and produce an indication that an overflow is detected. Your procedure should include a method to examine the contents of the accumulator and the carry flag after the addition has been completed.

2. Use the program of step 1 of the prelaboratory investigation to determine the checksum of the program itself.

3. Using the program of step 2 of the prelaboratory investigation, verify the answers from Cases 1 to 8 studied in the background investigation.

4. Add the following numbers using the routine of step 3 of the prelaboratory investigation:

    a) 01010111   c) 01011011

        + 01011011   + 00010101

    b) 01010111   d) 00100101

        + 00110110   + 01111111

5. Verify the correct operation of the programs from steps 4 and 5 of the prelaboratory investigation by using the following problems:

    a) 01101010 11101011   b) EFA4   c) 453F

        + 00001010 11010111   + 01DE   - 43FF

    d) FADC   e) 14F2   f) 00E4

        + 3F2C   - FCD1   + FACE

Questions for Further Study

1. Two's complement of a binary number is defined as the number that must be added to the original number to equal zero. Is this also true for the ten's complement? How can the ten's complement be found?

2. Draw a simple flowchart to perform floating point addition.

3. What are the ranges of signed numbers, in base 10, when a 16 bit word length is used? In octal? In hexidecimal?

Experiment 5

INPUT/OUTPUT: LOGIC SIMULATIONS

Purpose

This experiment will investigate the use of input/output statements as well as the use of logical statements to simulate various
TTL integrated circuit configurations.

Background Investigation

A computer system without input/output capabilities serves no
useful purpose. It cannot accept inquiries or input data nor can it
respond with control signals or answers to problems. Input/output
is very important because it represents the only form of communications
most users see. The ability for a system to be accepted by the users
is often judged solely on the basis of its I/O capability and not the
internal integrity of the system. System designers should carefully
plan the I/O configurations to adapt well to the problem solution.

Input/output operations are treated in a variety of ways on
different microprocessor systems. They usually fall into two specific categories: 1) processors which have specific I/O instructions and 2) processors which use a portion of memory to act as an
I/O port or location. The latter category is referred to as memory
mapped I/O.

The processors which have specific instructions such as IN or
OUT usually communicate to an I/O port over the data bus while the
address of a specific port is given via the address bus. In cases
such as this, the port designation is specified as part of the instruction, usually as the second word. The contents of the accumulator are then transferred to the output device (OUT instruction),
or, in the case of an IN instruction, the input port's contents are
transferred to the accumulator.

Memory mapped I/O processors use instructions such as LOAD and
STORE to send or retrieve data from the ports. These are the same
instructions that transfer data from the accumulator to or from
memory. In fact, it is difficult to tell if a program is performing
I/O or reads or writes to memory without looking into the hardware
configuration.

30

Some I/O ports also have additional lines that signal the condition of the port, such as: data available, processor in an output write cycle, status bits, etc. These control signals, called handshake lines, may be read by interrogating another port. Once in the accumulator, these signals may be appropriately interpreted. It is also important to determine if the output port associated with the processor has latching capability. If not, when the output cycle is complete, the data will be lost unless it is latched by some external device. Once the latches are installed, data can only be changed by re-writing to the output port.

Microcomputer systems may employ a programmable I/O device such as the PIA (Peripheral Interface Adapter) which allows anyone of 16 lines to operate as either input or output. These lines are programmed by writing into specific auxiliary ports designated for this purpose. Additional handshaking lines are available.

The logical instruction subset of the processor can be very useful in performing many of the functions necessary to provide the desired control. In addition, logical instructions are used in the processing of numerical and flag data. The first instruction to be investigated is the AND function.

Consider that two data words, one in memory and one stored in the accumulator, are to be ANDed together. The truth table for the AND function can be recalled as:

A	B	OUTPUT
0	0	0
0	1	0
1	0	0
1	1	1

This is the normal process involving only two single bit words. When the processor performs this function, however, it does so with an entire word but still on a bit by bit basis.

        01011001 (accumulator)

        10111011 (memory)

        00011001 (result placed in accumulator)

The AND function may also be used to mask a particular portion of the word in the accumulator--that is, to disregard bit positions of no interest and leave only those bits in the accumulator that are important. If an input word to the accumulator appears as shown below, where D represents those bits which are to be discarded and C, those to be retained, it may be ANDed with 00001111 to yield a word

in the accumulator that will always have the high order four bits set
to zero.

DDDDCCCC (accumulator)

00001111 (mask word)

0000CCCC (result in accumulator)

Whatever C represents, it will remain unchanged after the masking.

1011 1010

0000 1111   same value

0000 1010

This procedure may be employed to mask a single or multiple bits.

The logical OR function acts in a similar manner to the bit OR
function but again, operates on an entire word on a bit by bit basis.

1011 0101 (accumulator)

1010 1101 (memory)

1011 1101 (result)

One process which may prove useful to recall in some programming
operations is that if the accumulator is zero, ORing a word will load
that word into the accumulator.

0000 0000 (A)

1010 1101 (M)

1010 1101 (R)

The exclusive OR follows the same guidelines as previously discussed. Recall, the exclusive OR truth table to be:

A	B	OUTPUT
0	0	0
0	1	1
1	0	1
1	1	0

For an eight bit word, it would be:

$$0011\ 0101\quad (A)$$

$$\underline{1010\ 1011}\quad (M)$$

$$1001\ 1110\quad (R)$$

The exclusive OR is sometimes used to clear the accumulator in processors which do not have a CLEAR instruction. If the accumulator is exclusive ORed with itself, the result will always be zero.

$$1011\ 1101\quad (A)$$

$$\underline{1011\ 1101}\quad (M)$$

$$0000\ 0000\quad (R)$$

The complement function may be used similar to the NOT function in Boolean algebra. It will cause each of the bits stored in the accumulator to be inverted.

$$1010\ 1010\quad \text{before complement}$$

$$0101\ 0101\quad \text{after complement}$$

This procedure effectively forms the one's complement of the number. When used in conjunction with other instructions, it can be used to form the two's complement, convert negative logic inputs to positive logic and perform NAND and NOR operations.

The last group of logical instructions provides the ability to rotate the accumulator either right or left. Most of these instructions involve the carry bit in some way or another. Two groups of rotate instructions can be found on most processors; one rotates the bits through the carry position and the other does not. Consider the rotate left through carry. The status of the accumulator before and after the rotate is shown below.

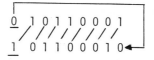

Note that each bit of the word is rotated left one position, the MSB is moved into the carry position and the LSB becomes the previous carry.

The other form of rotate instruction can be illustrated as follows. Each bit is again rotated left one position and the MSB becomes the carry bit, but the MSB also becomes the LSB of the word.

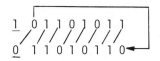

In this case, the value of the carry bit is lost.

Rotate instructions prove very useful when employed to do such operations as multiply or divide by powers of two, check the status of specific bits, in binary multiply and divide routines or in code conversion schemes.

Obviously, the logical instructions discussed thus far can be used to simulate simple logic gates such as AND, OR, NOT, and EXCLUSIVE OR, but they may also be used to simulate NAND and NOR gates as well. Consider the simulation of the NAND function. If the inputs to the NAND gate are connected to the LSB and LSB+1 of the input port, the output is taken from the LSB of the output port and the remaining bits on the input and output ports are ignored; then the following procedure could be employed to simulate the NAND function.

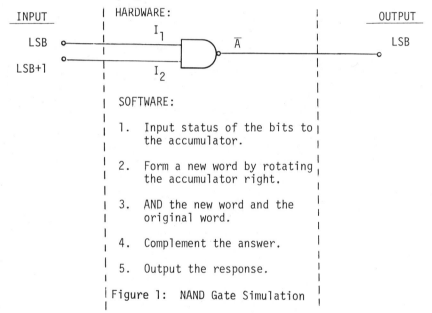

Figure 1: NAND Gate Simulation

The accumulator contents would appear as follows for each of the steps shown above. Ds are used to represent don't cares and I_1, I_2 are the gate inputs.

Step #1

$$\underline{0}\ \text{DDDDDD}I_1I_2$$

Step #2
$$I_2 \text{ ODDDDDDDI}_1$$

Step #3
$$I_2 \text{ DDDDDDDA} \quad (A=I_1I_2)$$

Step #4
$$I_2 \text{ DDDDDDD}\overline{A} \quad (\overline{A}=\overline{I_1I_2})$$

The status of the carry bit and the other bits in the word are not important and will not affect the result. Masking may be employed to insure that all of the don't care bits are set to zero before the final output instruction. If the NAND function is to be performed on an entire word, the process would be the same, except that the rotate would not be necessary due to the fact that the data would already be in two separate words.

An entire integrated circuit may be simulated by this method. Consider the diagram below which represents a 7400, quad two input NAND gate.

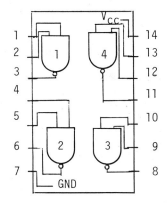

Figure 2: 7400 IC

If the inputs and outputs are properly connected, most of the programming problems can be eliminated. If the input data word is constructed as follows:

$$I_1I_1I_2I_2I_3I_3I_4I_4$$

and the output data word as

$$DA_1DA_2DA_3DA_4$$

the same procedure can be followed as shown in Figure 1. The actual data flow would be as follows:

Step #1

$$\underline{0}\; I_1I_1I_2I_2I_3I_3I_4I_4 \quad \text{(input data)}$$

Step #2

$$\underline{I_4}0I_1I_1I_2I_2I_3I_3I_4 \quad \text{(rotate right)}$$

Step #3

$$\underline{I_4}DA_1DA_2DA_3DA_4 \qquad \text{(logical AND)}$$
$$(A_x = I_x I_x)$$

Step #4

$$\underline{I_4}D\overline{A}_1D\overline{A}_2D\overline{A}_3D\overline{A}_4 \qquad \text{(complement)}$$
$$(\overline{A}_x = I_x I_x)$$

Again, if the D (don't care) terms are a problem on output, they may be subsequently masked to zero.

More complicated TTL equivalents may be simulated using these methods. However, it is important to remember that the simulation will not operate exactly as the real device. The speed at which the processor executes instructions will adversely affect the speed of the simulation. They are functionally equivalent, however.

Consider the 74121 monostable multivibrator. Based on the inputs, A_1, A_2 and B, it provides an output at Q for a length of time that is a function of the timing components R-C. A trigger signal begins the action of the one shot. Once the process has begun, additional trigger signals will not affect the output. Such a monostable is referred to as non-retriggerable. If subsequent triggers do affect the output by extending the delay time by an appropriate amount, it is said to be retriggerable. Only the non-retriggerable case will be studied here. The diagram for the 74121 is shown below.

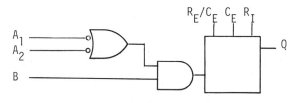

Figure 3:   The 74121

Inputs A_1 and A_2 are negative edge triggered while input B is positive edge triggered. In both cases, the one shot pulse out occurs only if the inputs are in the proper configuration and the appropriate input changes state. The truth table for this process is

36

shown below. D represents a don't care term.

A_1	A_2	B	OUTPUT
0	D	1	0
D	0	1	0
D	D	0	0
1	1	D	0
1	⌐↓	1	One Shot
⌐↓	1	1	One Shot
⌐↓	⌐↓	1	One Shot
L	D	_↑	One Shot
D	L	_↑	One Shot

In the cases above, the important conditions that are necessary before the one shot can occur must be met along with the appropriate transitional characteristic.

The procedure for checking for a high to low transition may best be described by the flowchart given below. Note the use of the masking procedure previously discussed. This may be modified slightly to reduce program size by using rotate instructions in conjunction with the carry bit if the bit position to be checked is either the MSB or LSB (fewer rotates required).

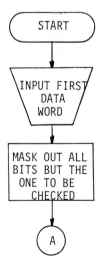

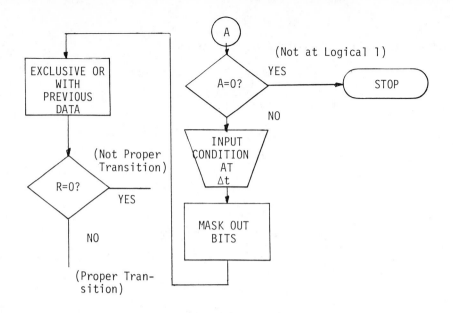

Figure 4: Negative Edge Trigger Checking Routine

A procedure to check for a low to high transition can be constructed by simply modifying the first decision block in Figure 4 and testing for a nonzero condition.

The triggering procedure outlined in the table may be summarized in a shorter form as follows:

1. If the B input is high and either or both of the A inputs go low - one shot.

2. If either or both of the A inputs are low and B goes high - one shot.

The entire procedure is outlined in Figure 5 by the flowchart representation.

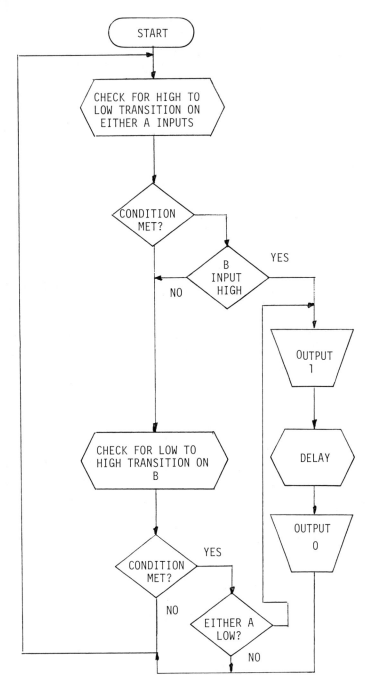

Figure 5: Monostable Program

Prelaboratory Investigation

1. Determine the I/O configuration for your particular processor configuration. Is it instruction oriented or memory mapped?

2. Many hours of program debugging time can be saved by first checking out the interface hardware (where the problem usually begins). Write a short routine, assuming the output lines are connected to the input lines, to check out both the input and output ports on a bit by bit basis. The program should indicate the outcome of this functional test.

3. Write a program to simulate a 7402, quad two input NOR gate.

4. Implement the flowcharts for the 74121 monostable multivibrator. The pulse width for your program should be variable. From the manufacturer's specifications, determine the maximum and minimum delay times. Project how closely your program will match these specifications.

5. Simulate a three line to eight line decoder multiplexer integrated circuit. This circuit operation is similar to a 74154 integrated circuit.

6. List the advantages and disadvantages of simulating the operation of TTL integrated circuits. What do you consider to be the biggest advantage?

Laboratory Investigation

1. Upon application of power on initial start-up, do the output lines always begin at the same state? Why or why not?

2. Check the operation of the input and output ports by using the program written in step 2 of the prelaboratory analysis.

3. Using the program written in step 3 of the prelaboratory analysis, experimentally determine the maximum "propagation delay" of this simulation. Could this answer have been predicted using the timing information from the instruction specifications?

4. Experimentally determine the shortest pulse width obtainable for the 74121 simulation.

5. Verify the correct operation of the multiplexer simulation from the prelaboratory analysis in step 5.

Questions for Further Study

1. The retriggerable monostable may be simulated provided that the
    trigger conditions may be constantly checked during the delay.
    What methods are available to do this on the microprocessor?

2. How may the pulse width of the 74121 simulation be shortened?
    Is it possible to duplicate the manufacturer's specifications
    on pulse width? Why or why not?

3. Draw a flowchart to simulate a master slave J-K flip-flop.

4. Simulate a BCD to seven segment decoder driver. What advantages
    would simulating this device have over an integrated circuit
    version in an actual application?

5. Which TTL functions are most difficult to simulate? Are there
    any that are impossible to simulate?

Experiment 6

BCD ARITHMETIC AND CONVERSIONS

Purpose

The intent of this experiment is to investigate BCD addition and subtraction. In addition a binary to BCD conversion program will be written.

Background Investigation

Basic arithmetic operations performed by the computer are carried out using the binary number system. Fortunately the operations implemented are easily constructed using relatively simple logic circuits. The interface that must be provided to the outside world however, is most often decimal rather than binary. This necessitates an additional step in the cycle of processing data. Obviously a binary to decimal conversion routine would accomplish this but internal processing would still be done in binary. Codes to represent base 10 numbers in binary have been developed and many are presented in this manual.

Many microprocessor based test instruments and digital interfacable devices use a weighted code to represent the decimal numbers. This Binary Coded Decimal format is used in many instrumentation devices. Many weighted codes are available but the most common is the 8-4-2-1 code and will be treated exclusively here.

It is a simple task to convert decimal to BCD or vice versa for one who is familiar with hexidecimal or even octal notation. Each decimal position is converted into a form bit binary number using the 8-4-2-1 weight of its position.

$$841_{10} = (1000\ 0100\ 0001)_{BCD}$$

This procedure allows internal machine representation in a decimal manner, more easily readable and with the added ability to simplify communications with external devices. Procedures have been developed to perform simple arithmetic operations with these numbers while maintaining their form. Operations using straight binary representation, although less representative of decimal notation, still are the most efficient and continue to be widely used. The BCD format is also less efficient due to the fact that out of the 16 possible combinations in a four bit binary number, only 10 are used. Even with these drawbacks, the positive features of BCD representation and its continued use in test instruments make it worthy of study.

Using a specially developed set of rules, binary adders can be used to perform BCD addition. The process can best be shown by an example. Because the word length of most microprocessors is eight bits, two BCD digits may be formed. A maximum decimal value of 99 can be represented.

Decimal	BCD
54	0101 0100
+ 13	+ 0001 0011
67	0110 0111

In the case above, no special rules are necessary because no carry was generated from the right most four bits to the left most four bits and the result for both number positions is less than nine.

Decimal	BCD
48	0100 1000
+ 16	+ 0001 0110
64	0101 1110

The addition shown above has produced a non-allowable value for the right most four bits. In this case six may be added to the low order position and the carry propagated to the high order BCD value as in straight binary addition.

$$0101\ 1110$$

$$+0110$$

$$0110\ 0100$$

This produces the correct result. For the example shown below, note that when the carry takes place from the low four bits, this is a signal to add six to form the correct BCD digit.

Decimal	BCD
	1 (Carry)
59	0101 1001
+ 29	+ 0010 1001
88	1000 0010

$$\underline{+\ 0110}$$

$$1000\ 1000$$

It can be proven that the addition of six of the low order value, if the number is greater than nine or if a carry exists between the low order and high order terms, will always form a BCD formatted number for the result. It should be pointed out that the two numbers to be added should be in BCD format initially.

This rule also applies to the high order four bits as in the following example.

Decimal	BCD
45	0100 0101
+ 71	+ 0111 0001
116	1011 0110
	(result not BCD)
	+ 0110
	1 0001 0110
	(Carryout Produced)

The carryout obtained in the above example indicates an overflow condition and can be used to form a double precision BCD value when added to the next significant word.

Note the importance of the carry produced from the low order to the high order terms. This carry is given its own name in microprocessor systems that perform BCD operations. It is called the half carry or auxiliary carry. The carry out of the high order terms is the standard accumulator overflow available on all machines.

The decimal adjust accumulator instruction, employed to facilitate BCD addition, follows the same set of rules as outlined above. It may be more succinctly stated as follows:

When two BCD formatted numbers are added in the accumulator using an add instruction, the accumulator results may be adjusted to form two BCD digits by the following process:

1. If the value of the least significant four bits of the accumulator is greater than or if the half carry flag is set, 6 is added to the accumulator.

2. If the value of the most significant four bits of the accumulator is now greater than nine or if the carry flag is set, add six to the most significant four bits.

BCD subtraction may be conducted in a similar manner as complement addition in normal binary notation. However, the ten's complement is used. The ten's complement may be thought of as the nine's
complement plus one. The example below will depict the subtraction
process.

Decimal	BCD
47	0100 0111
- 12	- 0001 0010

The ten's complement may be found by taking the nine's complement,
99-12 = 87, and adding 1 = 88.

99	1001 1001
- 12	- 0001 0010
87	1000 0111
+ 1	+ 1
88	1000 1000

Now, the subtraction process may be completed using the previously discussed addition procedure.

47	0100 0111
+ 88	1000 1000
1 35	1100 1111

+0110   decimal adjust
                function
1 0101
(half carry)
1100 0101

+1

+ 0110
$\boxed{1}$ 0011

0011 0101

(The carry out may be discarded as in the case with normal binary two's
complement addition.)

This process works well except when the number that is being sub-tracted (subtrahend) is greater than the number from which it is sub-tracted (minuend). The procedure unfortunately breaks down at this point. The procedure for continuing is very involved and hence, its lack of wide use. Multiplication and division can also be performed when the numbers are in BCD format but due, again, to the relative complexity are rarely used. In these cases, conversion to binary is often employed. Subsequent conversion back to BCD then yields the desired result.

A conversion to BCD from binary may be done by repeated addition of one to an initially zeroed accumulator followed by a decimal ad-just instruction. The originally zeroed accumulator is in BCD format and the 1 added is also in BCD format. These are the two prerequi-sites necessary for the decimal adjust instruction to work properly. With every subtraction, one is subtracted from the original binary number until it reaches zero. Of course, if an eight bit word is used, the original binary number must be less than 99 or double pre-cision numbers will result.

The flowchart given below will better illustrate this procedure. It has been assumed that the value is $\leq 99_{10}$.

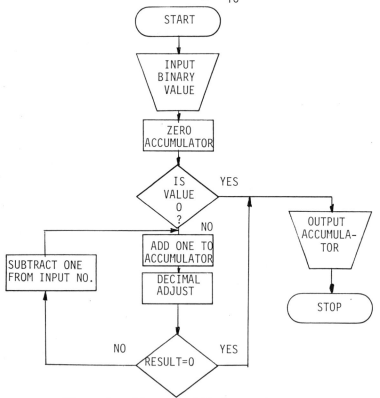

Figure 1: Binary to BCD Conversion

Prelaboratory Investigation

1. The procedure for BCD addition is quite straightforward using the decimal adjust accumulator instruction. Write a short flowchart and program to do BCD addition for a double precision number.

2. Justify or correct the equations necessary to perform the decimal adjust operation on an n digit value given below:

   If $S_i = A_i + B_i + C_{i-1} < 10$ no alteration necessary

   If $S_i = A_i + B_i + C_{i-1} \geq 10$ then $S_i = S_i + 6$

3. Write a subroutine to perform the subtraction process outlined in the background section. Note: The program should insure that there is not a subtraction of a larger number from a smaller number.

4. Using the subroutine outlined above, write a short BCD to binary conversion program.

5. Devise a list of BCD based devices and instruments. Be as specific as possible.

6. Do the devices listed in step 5 above use BCD format for internal logic or straight binary?

Laboratory Investigation

1. Verify the correct operation of the program in step 1 of the prelaboratory investigation. Try all possible cases for carry and half carry bit status. Explain the range of values that may be added.

2. Test the subroutine written in step 3 of the prelaboratory investigation for all possibilities of input value ranges.

3. Couple the binary to BCD conversion program outlined in figure 1 to the program written in step 4 of the prelaboratory investigation and run the programs with random binary input values to insure its correct operation.

Questions for Further Study

1. How can a double precision BCD format number be easily multiplied by 10? By 2?

2. Other than repeated addition, is there another method that can be used to do binary to BCD conversion?

47

3. What are the advantages and disadvantages of using the repeated addition method of BCD conversion verses other techniques?

4. Assume a test instrument forwards a 3 1/2 digit BCD value to the computer for processing. In order to determine the correct value, the computer must multiply by 3/2. Draw a general flowchart depicting the process necessary to accomplish this.

5. What would be the maximum amount of storage required to save the answer of question 4 above?

6. Are there any advantages to using a four bit processor to perform BCD operations?

Experiment 7

PUSH BUTTON INTERFACE - BCD COUNTING

Purpose

In this experiment, an investigation of the operation of a push button and the decimal adjust accumulator instruction will be investigated. A 0-99 BCD counter will be constructed.

Background Investigation

One of the most readily available devices used to interface the outside world is the push button. The inherent 1-0 action makes it ideal for incorporation into a binary system. However, the mechanical action of the switch makes its operation somewhat less practical to use.

This mechanical action of the push button causes the contacts to bounce when the button is depressed. Although the bounce may not be perceivable in many applications, the problem is magnified due to the speed of the microprocessor and it may count every bounce. The bounce may last from several to a few hundred milliseconds depending on the configuration of the device. A maximum bounce time is usually specified in the manufacturer's literature.

Several procedures have been developed to debounce a push button using external logic and delay elements. The circuit shown below is a standard R-S flip-flop that toggles the output depending on the state

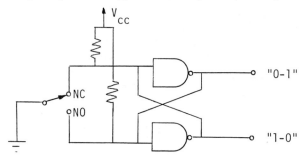

Figure 1: Basic Debounce Circuit

of the input switch. One drawback of this configuration, besides the additional hardware needed in the application, is the need for a double pole switch.

Two similar circuits for switch debouncing are shown below using inverters and a D flip-flop.

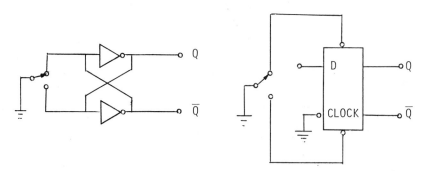

Figure 2: Inverters and Flip-flops Used in Debouncing

A monostable multivibrator or one-shot may be employed to provide a predetermined delay. The push button may be connected to the one-shot as shown below with the appropriate delay (as determined from the manufacturer's specifications) set by R and C external. The one-shot will trigger the output ON on the first detection of a contact closure. In a nonretriggerable one-shot, subsequent bounces in the push button will not affect the output since the output will remain ON until the delay time has expired.

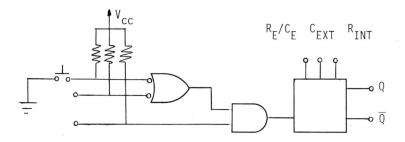

Figure 3: Monostable Debounce Circuit

It is also important to keep in mind that the duty cycle, as specified in the data sheets, is an additional limitation. One-shots need time to recover after they have been fired. Duty cycle may be defined as:

$$\text{Duty Cycle} = \frac{T_{ON}}{T_{ON} + T_{OFF}}$$

The microprocessor software version of the push button debouncer has some advantages. It does not require the additional hardware for implementation and can be written as a subroutine thus enabling it to be used for many switch applications. If, in the particular application, however, PROM space is at a premium, debouncing may be left to the hardware.

A simple software procedure may be used to provide the switch delay used in debouncing. The flowchart is given below.

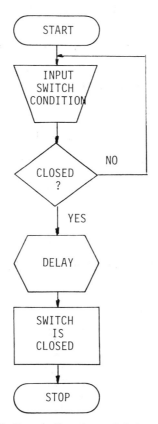

Figure 4: Software Version of Debounce

When the microprocessor is used to count switch closures, the switch status must be monitored for openings as well as closures to insure that valid counts will be tallied. The speed with which the microprocessor executes instructions will result in multiple counts if the switch is only polled for closures.

Obviously, the delay routine should be long enough to insure that all switch bounces have ceased. To be sure of this, a delay of, say, 200 microseconds could be used. Even the fastest button push would be at least this long thus insuring the correct count.

In the BCD counting program used in this experiment, the decimal adjust accumulator instruction will be employed to provide the proper output. An investigation of the manufacturer's literature will show a complicated procedure outlining how the processor performs this operation employing the half or auxiliary carry. The purpose and result of using the decimal adjust instruction may be summarized as follows: When an add instruction is used to sum two already BCD numbers, the decimal adjust instruction will insure the result is BCD.

In the BCD counting program for this experiment, the decimal adjust will be valid if:

   a) the count to be updated is stored in the accumulator,

   b) the count is in BCD format (this is no problem initially if 00 is used to start),

   c) the increment is in BCD format (01 is already BCD),

   d) an add instruction is used, and

   e) the decimal adjust follows the add instruction.

If the above procedure is followed, the resulting value will be in BCD.

Prelaboratory Investigation

A flowchart to implement the counter program is given below. Note that the switch is monitored for an opening as well as a closure.

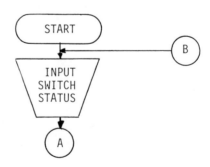

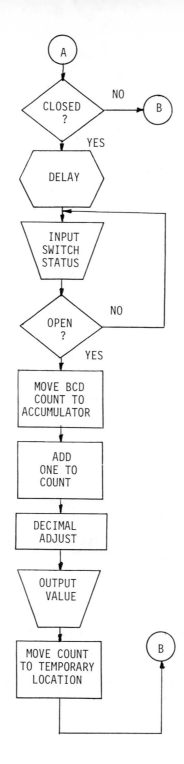

Figure 5: BCD
Counting
Program

The hardware interface diagram given below will show the procedure for interface of the switch and output displays. The displays, as shown, include the circuitry for the decoder/drivers.

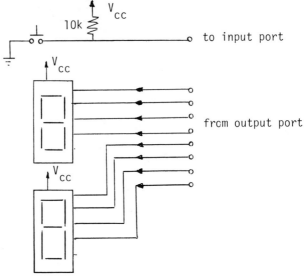

Figure 6: Hardware Interface Diagram

1. Code the flowchart given into machine language. A previously developed delay routine may be employed.

2. Determine an appropriate delay time for the switch used. Consult the manufacturer's literature, if available.

3. Investigate the type of seven segment displays to be used in this experiment and determine the correct wiring to the appropriate decoder/driver circuitry.

Laboratory Investigation

1. Construct the hardware interface to be used in this experiment.

2. Verify the correct operation of the program.

3. Remove the 10 k resistor from the input switch and note any change in operation.

4. With the debounce portion of the program removed, use the program
    to actually count the number of switch bounces for various
    switches.

5. Determine which portion(s) of this program should be coded into
    a subroutine for multiple switch inputs.

6. Construct the circuits of Figures 1 and 2. Interface these to
    the microprocessor and the BCD counting program with the software
    debounce portion removed.

Questions for Further Study

1. What purpose does the resistor on the input switch serve?

2. Besides an I/O port, what other means may be used to interface
    the switch to the microprocessor?

3. Does it matter if hex displays are used in place of the decimal
    displays used in this experiment? Why?

4. If the switch were debounced externally, what effect would
    this have on the size of the program?

5. Using the manufacturer's specifications for the 74121, determine
    the appropriate timing elements to provide a 100 millisecond
    delay for the circuit of Figure 3.

Experiment 8

LOGIC DESIGN

Purpose

The purpose of this experiment is to become familiar with trade-offs between logic design with hardware and software.

Background Investigation

In many applications, microprocessor systems may be used to re-place gates and flip-flop elements with software. Although economics may dictate the design should be implemented in discrete logic, the microprocessor based system provides added flexibility not available with hardwired systems. In addition, if the microprocessor is already part of the system design it seems reasonable to use it to replace as much of the external hardware as possible.

It has been said that 8 to 16 bytes of memory are the logical equivalent of a single gate. Assuming that the IC used today contains, on the order of 10 gates, then one can conclude that logic can be stored in memory in a cost effective manner for large systems. In addition, changes can be easily implemented in microprocessor systems. The table shown in figure 1 summarizes these design and development considerations.

The reduced cost of custom LSI circuitry has added another phase to this already complex problem. Custom circuits for large volume applications are becoming increasingly popular due to new integrated circuit manufacturing techniques which produce higher yields and less setup time.

The appropriate decision is not always clear and many times not evident until one is too far along to reconsider. In an attempt to provide some familiarization with this area, several simple examples of both hardware and software implementations will be presented in this experiment.

An example of a simple design of the type mentioned follows:

A photo cell instrument is measuring the length of bolts from 0 to 9 inches in one inch increments. The instrument is capable of producing binary outputs 0-9 which correspond to the length of the bolt being measured. Design a logic network which causes a "reject" lamp to light when the part measured is not of the length 2, 4, 6 or 8 inches.

A truth table indicating the desired outputs is shown in figure 2.

Steps in the Development of a Product/System	Hardwired Logic	Programmed Logic
1. Problem Definition		Simplified due to the ease of incorporating features.
2. System Design	Logic Diagrams (Components)	Algorithm Development
3. Debugging & Testing	Laboratory Instrumentation (Hardware Modifications are costly)	Software modifications are easy to implement.
4. PC Board Layout		Fewer boards to lay out
5. Power Consumption	Power Requirements vary	Typically low power consumption
6. Engineering Changes	Wiring Modifications	Modify program
7. Documentation	Troubleshooting procedures often difficult to document	Diagnostics may be programmed into the system

Figure 1: Design Considerations

First, the hardware logic diagram may be constructed followed by a software implementation. A karnaugh map may be used to provide a simplified logic expression for this system.

A	B	C	D	REJECT
0	0	0	0	1
0	0	0	1	1
0	0	1	0	0
0	0	1	1	1
0	1	0	0	0
0	1	0	1	1
0	1	1	0	0
0	1	1	1	1
1	0	0	0	0
1	0	0	1	1
1	0	1	0	DC
1	0	1	1	DC
1	1	0	0	DC
1	1	0	1	DC
1	1	1	0	DC
1	1	1	1	DC

These are don't care terms.

Figure 2: Photo Cell Instrument Output

		C	0	1	0	1
A	B	D	0	0	1	1
0	0		1	0	1	1
0	1		0	0	1	1
1	0		0	DC	1	DC
1	1		DC	DC	DC	DC

Figure 3: Karnaugh Map

The logic expression for this circuit can be reduced to

$$R = D + \overline{A}\ \overline{B}\ \overline{C}$$

and could be implemented in NAND logic by the following:

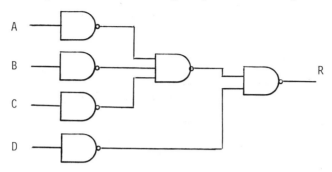

Figure 4:   NAND Implementation

A software flowchart for the same procedure is shown in figure 5. Note that this procedure may be easily modified for any set of measurements.

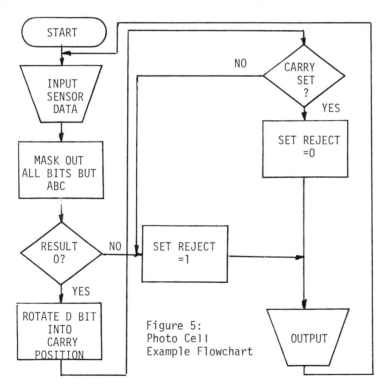

Figure 5:
Photo Cell
Example Flowchart

Prelaboratory Investigation

1. A transfer arm T on a conveyor is to sort parts according to the following criterion furnished by binary input:

   Weight: 0 is light; 1 is heavy
   Color: 0 is white; 1 is black
   Height: 0 is short; 1 is tall
   Diameter: 0 is small; 1 is large

   T is 1 and the parts are transferred off the conveyor when the part satisfies anyone of the following light criterion:

   a) large, heavy, black and short

   b) small, tall, heavy and black

   c) light, white, short and small

   d) tall, white, light and small

   e) large, heavy, small and white

   f) tall, heavy, small and white

   g) large, black, light and short

   h) large, light, white and short

   Implement the above conditions using a minimal NAND logic configuration.

2. Design a software system to accomplish the same task as step 1 above.

3. The following BCD code is called "two-out-of-five code" and is used for the detection of errors.

Decimal Value	Code Word				
	A	B	C	D	E
0	0	0	0	1	1
1	0	0	1	0	1
2	0	1	0	0	1
3	1	0	0	0	1
4	0	0	1	1	0
5	0	1	0	1	0
6	1	0	0	1	0
7	0	1	1	0	0
8	1	0	1	0	0
9	1	1	0	0	0

   Design a combinational logic system that detects an error whenever an erroneous combination is present.

4. Program the microprocessor to accomplish the same task as in step 3 above.

5. Parity is often used to determine if an incoming data word contains errors. A parity bit is added to the word based on the following set of rules.

   1. For even parity, the extra bit is set to insure the total number of bits in the word is even,

   2. For odd parity, the extra bit is set to insure the total number of bits in the word is odd.

   It has been assumed when working with this system that only one bit in the word would be in error.

   Devise a hardware scheme to check the parity of an eight bit word assuming seven bits of data and the eighth bit (MSB) would be the parity bit for even parity. (Hint: Use exclusive-OR logic.)

6. Program the procedure outlined in step 5 above.

Laboratory Investigation

1. Test both the logic implementation and the program for the conveyor sorting problem in steps 1 and 2 of the prelaboratory analysis. Do they both respond in identical manner?

2. Will speed of response be an important consideration in this application? Conduct a test to verify that speed is not a problem.

3. Verify the correct operation for the "two-out-of-five" error detector by operating both systems in parallel.

4. Discuss speed of response characteristics for these two implementations.

5. Verify the correct operation of the parity checking routine and logic circuit design.

Questions for Further Study

1. Develop a generalized procedure for the implementation of an eight variable truth table.

2. What would be the advantages and disadvantages for each system developed in this experiment when comparing the hardwired logic to the microprocessor based program in regard to cost, time, speed, etc.?

3. Can any generalized rules be developed dictating when to use hardware and when to use software in a particular application?

4. Should applications be developed where part of the design is microprocessor based and part discrete logic? When?

Experiment 9

SERIAL ASCII TO BCD CODE CONVERSION

Purpose

The purpose of this experiment is to investigate the use of the microprocessor for the conversion of one data format into another.

Background Investigation

Applications for the microprocessor include its use as an intelligent interface device between two devices. It could be called upon to convert data generated by one device in one format into a format readable by another. Such an application may require that the processor do any number of modifications to the data, parallel to serial, serial to parallel, code modifications and timing changes.

In this experiment, the microprocessor will be programmed to accept two eight bit ASCII numbers and convert them to their BCD equivalents. The ASCII codes for the digits 0-9 are given below for reference:

$$B0_{16} \rightarrow 260_8 \rightarrow 0 \rightarrow 0000_{BCD}$$

$$B1_{16} \rightarrow 261_8 \rightarrow 1 \rightarrow 0001$$

$$B2_{16} \rightarrow 262_8 \rightarrow 2 \rightarrow 0010$$

$$B3_{16} \rightarrow 263_8 \rightarrow 3 \rightarrow 0011$$

$$B4_{16} \rightarrow 264_8 \rightarrow 4 \rightarrow 0100$$

$$B5_{16} \rightarrow 265_8 \rightarrow 5 \rightarrow 0101$$

$$B6_{16} \rightarrow 266_8 \rightarrow 6 \rightarrow 0110$$

$$B7_{16} \rightarrow 267_8 \rightarrow 7 \rightarrow 0111$$

$$B8_{16} \rightarrow 270_8 \rightarrow 8 \rightarrow 1000$$

$$B9_{16} \rightarrow 271_8 \rightarrow 9 \rightarrow 1001$$

The process will begin as data for the first ASCII character is shifted into an internal register within the microprocessor one bit at a time as shown in the hardware diagram in figure 1. The data is obtained from the data switch next, the data ready signal is depressed. After the process is repeated eight times, the ASCII code for the first number will have been entered. It is now a simple process to subtract 260_8 from this number to convert the value to BCD.

The process is repeated until the second ASCII code is entered and the BCD value formed. Then, the two BCD digits are combined to form a single eight bit word and outputted. This process is described in the flowchart shown in figure 2.

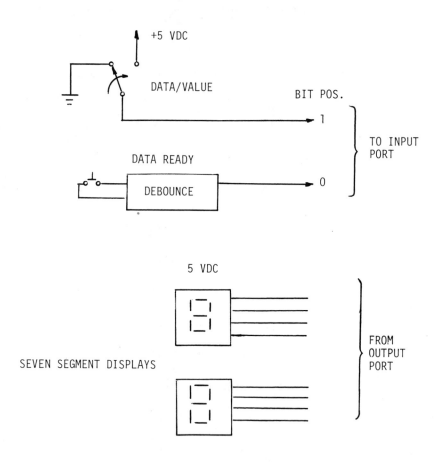

Figure 1: Hardware Interface Diagram

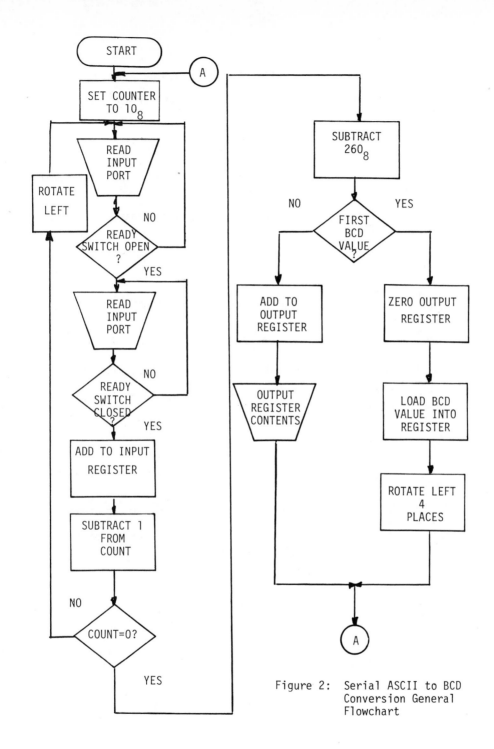

Figure 2: Serial ASCII to BCD
Conversion General
Flowchart

65

Prelaboratory Investigation

1. Code the flowchart shown in figure 2 into machine language.

2. Is there a shorter way of converting the eight bit ASCII code into BCD, other than subtracting 260_8?

3. Revise the program of step 1 above so that it contains the fewest number of bytes.

4. Write a short program which will test the hardware interface shown in figure 1.

5. What provisions does your program have to insure that only valid ASCII codes are converted?

Laboratory Investigation

1. Implement the hardware configuration shown in figure 1. Test the interface using the program developed in step 4 of the prelaboratory investigation.

2. Load the conversion program and verify its correct operation.

3. Test the program using at least three pairs of ASCII values.

4. Estimate the maximum speed at which the serial ASCII data and subsequent output may be used.

Questions for Further Study

1. Flowchart a procedure to convert input binary numbers into Gray code.

2. What is the Hamming code and in what applications is it used?

3. Can binary encoding be used to determine the relative position of a circular disc? How could it be done?

Experiment 10

KEYBOARD INPUT

Purpose

This experiment will investigate the various keyboard configurations and the methods used to input their data to the microprocessor.

Background Investigation

The purpose of any input device is the communication of people
oriented data to the computer. In addition, the data must usually be
converted in this process from an alphanumeric form to a binary form
for subsequent processing or storage. The processor must be programmed to input data at a rate determined by the input device.
Rarely can the microprocessor dictate the rate at which data arrives
at the input port. The processor must wait until a key is depressed
or a flag is set before it can proceed.

Switches may be interconnected in an array to form a keyboard
input device. These switches are most often single pole single throw
momentary contact devices of the normally open variety. Although
these keyboards may contain over 100 switches, our investigation will
be limited to those which are used for decimal or hexadecimal input
only. Others may provide ASCII input.

Various keyboard configurations are used, but two switch configurations are the most common. In the first configuration, the keys
are simply normally open switches with one side common to all switches.
This configuration may also be found on thumbwheel type selecting
switches.

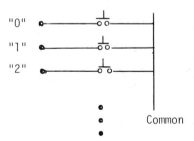

Figure 1: Common Connection

The second version is usually arranged as an nxm matrix of key switches (n rows and m columns). This configuration requires some type of decoding or encoding before the data can be transferred to the processor.

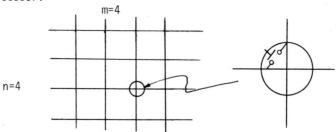

Figure 2: Array Connection

In the figure above, the switches form a 4x4 array which could represent a hexadecimal keypad, ideal for inputting data or instruction op codes into the processor for subsequent storage in memory.

The array connection is probably the most common keyboard form. For 16 switches, as in the case above, only 8 lines are needed. If the common connection of figure 1 were used, 16 lines would be needed. For either case, some reductions in lines can be made if some additional hardware were employed to perform the encoding fuction.

To develop a better appreciation of the discussion of the software to follow, refer to figure 3 for a hardware oriented keyboard interface. In this example, the common connection will be used.

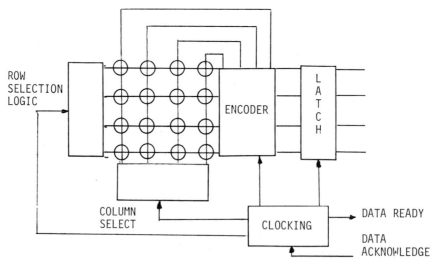

Figure 3: Hardware Keyboard Encoding

The clocking circuit begins by strobing the keyboard row and column lines waiting for a key to be depressed. The latch at this point is simply following the encoder output. The encoder may be a read only memory that uses the row and column lines for addressing information and produces a four bit word as an output. While the keyboard is being strobed, the DATA READY line is at a logic 0 indicating that no data is available. Once a key is depressed, the clocking circuit stops the strobing and causes the DATA READY line to go to a logic 1. At this point the data output from the encoder is also latched. The data remains in the latch until it is acknowledged via the DATA ACKNOWLEDGE line. Once this happens, the clocking circuit continues strobing until the next key is depressed. Note that in the event a key is depressed while the latches are locked, the data will be lost.

Although it is sometimes advantageous to use this hardware configuration when interfacing a keyboard to the microprocessor, many of these functions may be done by the software itself. Consider the following two sample keyboard interfaces.

Using the common connection type of keyboard, where all of the switches are normally open, the status of the switches may be simply connected to an input port as shown in figure 4. The pull-up resistors insure that the line status will always be high when the switches are open. When a switch is depressed, the appropriate input bit will go low. This type of configuration represents a negative logic input. The positive logic counterpart may be obtained after input by simply complementing the accumulator. Further processing, such as encoding and switch debouncing, may also be done by the software.

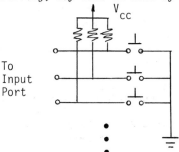

Figure 4:   Common Connection Input

This procedure, however, requires one dedicated input bit for each switch as well as one pull-up resistor. A keyboard with only ten switches would require ten input lines, not particularly well suited to an eight bit port. A more sophisticated procedure must therefore be developed.

An obvious method for combining inputs would be encoding. One such encoder may be developed using a 74150, 16 line to one line data selector/multiplexer. As shown below, this configuration requires only one input bit to the processor and four output bits from the output port.

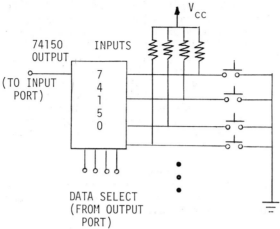

Figure 5: Encoding Circuit

The operation of the above circuit is as follows. The output four bits from the microcomputer is sent to the DATA SELECT input of the 74150. These bits select one of the 16 switches connected to the IC. If the switch is open (logical 1), then the output will be 0. If the switch is closed (logical 0), the output will be 1. The processor will be required to scan the keyboard one switch at a time until one is found that is depressed. At that time, the switch may be software debounced and the process repeated. Using this procedure, 16 switches may be handled using only 5 data lines (four output bits and one input bit). It still, however, has the disadvantage of requiring multiple pull-up resistors.

An additional method may be developed using the opposite method, i.e., a four line to 16 line decoder/demultiplexer. These types of integrated circuits are generally more readily available and do not require multiple pull-up resistors. A diagram of this configuration appears below. The IC employed here is 74154.

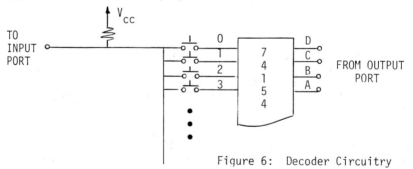

Figure 6: Decoder Circuitry

The 74154 uses a positive logic input and a negative logic output. When an input signal is applied to the terminals A,B,C,D, the corresponding terminal on the output will go to logic 0 while the other outputs will remain at 1. For example, if a 0010 were applied to the inputs (A=0,B=1,C=0,D=0), only the "2" output would go low, all others would remain at 1. Therefore, if switch 2 were depressed, the input bit to the processor would go to 0. Any other switch being depressed would have no effect. The processor would be required here again to provide a scanning signal. When the input bit does go to logical 0, the scanning count would be the value of the switch depressed. This method, as in the one previously discussed, requires only five data lines for up to 16 switches, but this method only uses one pull-up resistor. In the event a programmable I/O device is to be used for this interface, such as a PIA, four may be programmed for output and two for input thus greatly reducing the hardware interface.

A further refinement may be employed to scan the switches independently of the processor by using a MOD 16 counter and a clock circuit. The input to the processor may then be connected to the interrupt facility so the processor may be freed for other tasks.

Switch debouncing is required for all of these circuits in general, but a particular application may make it unnecessary. For example, if the switch depressed were displayed on a single, seven segment display, the lack of a debounce procedure would not be noticeable. When a switch is depressed, the multiple "depressions" resulting from the bounce would go unnoticed. Each bounce would cause the processor to write the same value on the display. However, if each depression were a portion of a longer number or phrase, the lack of debounce would produce many entries of the same value.

The nxm array connection can be interfaced to the processor in the following manner. The figure below shows the keyboard array and the connections to the I/O ports. Note that in this connection, several input and several output lines are used. The pull-up resistors insure the input lines will be at a logical 1 when no keys are depressed. When a logical 0 is applied to all columns of the keyboard from the output port, the input lines will be at a logical 1 until a key is depressed. Once the key depression is detected, the processor must then scan the keyboard, placing a 0 on each line, one at a time, until the appropriate column is detected. The rows will be at 1 unless the key depressed belongs in that row.

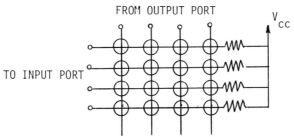

Figure 7: Array Connection Interface

Using this keyboard and minimum external hardware would require four output lines and four input lines to interface. Again, a single eight bit programmable interface device could be employed. This procedure requires the processor to scan the keyboard constantly looking for a closure. If interrupts are to be used, a few additional hardware items may be employed. Multiple key depressions may be resolved in the software by searching for the first closure only. Debouncing may also be done by the software.

A MOD 16 counter may be added with an appropriate clocking circuit to conduct the scan independent of the processor. In addition, a simple OR gate may be used to interrupt the processor if any key is depressed.

A flowchart for inputting and scanning this keyboard may be found in figure 8. Note the debounce delay. This should be done as soon as possible to avoid attempting to search for a closure during the bounce period. Multiple closures may be flagged at this point and either ignored or further deciphered in the software.

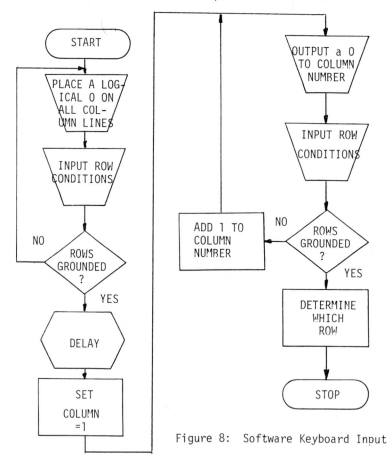

Figure 8: Software Keyboard Input

72

Once the row and column value is determined, the exact key depressed is known. Further decoding of this key may be done in a simple table look-up or other scheme.

If a programmable I/O port is employed, a procedure which requires less processor time can be used. If a 0 is outputted to all the columns and the row inputs are measured, and then a 0 is outputted to all the rows and the column inputs are measured, the precise key depressed can be determined.

Prelaboratory Investigation

1. Implement the hardware and write the program which will input a single depression of one of the keyboard configurations discussed in this experiment. The resulting key value should be displayed on a seven segment display.

2. Using the program from step 1, input a series of four BCD two digit numbers into memory.

3. Using the program above, as a subroutine, write a program which will enter hex data into memory. Note, this procedure may be placed in PROM and used to enter machine language programs. The following procedure may be used to implement this program.

   a) Enter the starting address in hex (exactly four numbers).

   b) Enter the data to be stored (two hex values) in order.

   c) Provide a feedback display to insure the proper values are being stored.

   d) Devise a scheme to correct false entries.

4. Classify each keyboard and program configuration discussed as to hardware required, processor time needed and program length. Describe applications which would be suited to each.

Laboratory Investigation

1. Verify the correct operation of the keyboard entry program as discussed in the prelaboratory investigation.

2. Test your program by attempting multiple key closures. How do the program and hardware react? What can be done to improve the response of the program?

3. Determine the fastest response time for your program to detect a key closure. Is there a possibility that a key closure may go undetected? What can be done to insure this will not happen?

4. If the microcomputer you are using utilizes a keyboard for primary input, investigate and document the hardware and software used.

Questions for Further Study

1. Devise a test circuit which will measure the speed with which a key may be closed and opened. Document this response time and project the shortest duration.

2. Using the keyboard described in figure 6, design additional hardware which will make this input device compatible with the interrupt facility.

3. Design a program to operate a digital combination lock which could be used to deactivate an electric door lock. A minimum four digit code should be used.

Experiment 11

HEXADECIMAL ADDITION/SUBTRACTION PROGRAM

Purpose

In this experiment a routine will be developed to perform hexadecimal addition and subtraction.

Background Investigation

The ability to add and subtract hexadecimal numbers is invaluable
in the design of microprocessor based systems. The calculation of offset addresses or simply the ease of checking a data calculation will
shorten program debugging time. In this experiment, a program to perform double precision hexadecimal calculations will be developed.
Eventually, this program could be placed on PROM and kept for future
use as the need arises.

The input output procedures for this experiment have previously
been discussed in other experiments. The output display will appear
as follows:

FFFF

Each of the characters will be shown on a seven segment display module.
Since the calculations will be performed in double precision, a total
of four displays will be needed. The displays may be multiplexed as
previously discussed, or each may be connected to four bit groups of
two eight bit, parallel output ports.

The input to this system will be accomplished using a hexadecimal
keypad configured similar to the one shown below.

1	2	3	F
4	5	6	E
7	8	9	D
0	A	B	C

In the development of the algorithms for this process, it should be noted that the only decoding/encoding that will be necessary is from the keyboard input. The operations that take place internally will already be in hexadecimal notation. A general flowchart depicting the procedure to be followed is shown in figure 1. Keyboard debounce will follow the same procedure as previously discussed in another experiment.

The process for performing an addition or subtraction will be as follows:

1. Enter the first number (the form will be 0001, 01FF, AB2F, etc.). Four keys will always be depressed and the number will be displayed as it is entered.

2. The display should show all zeros indicating the value has been received.

3. Enter the second number, following the same procedure as the first.

4. The display should again show all zeros.

5. At this point various options should be available and may be indicated to the processor by a single keystroke.

   1 = display first number

   2 = display the second number

   E = reenter the first number

   F = reenter the second number

   C = clear and start over

   A = add the two numbers

   B = subtract the second from the first

   D = subtract the first from the second

6. Answers should be displayed until the next command is given.

7. Continue to scan the keyboard to determine the next course of action as per step 5 above.

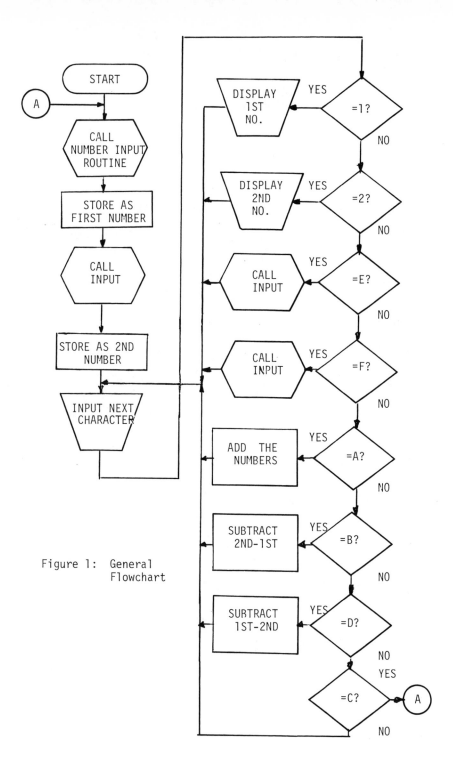

Figure 1:   General
            Flowchart

77

Prelaboratory Investigation

1. Develop a specific hardware interface for this system.

2. Draw a more specific flowchart for each of the routines shown in figure 1.

3. Code the hexadecimal addition/subtraction program.

Laboratory Investigation

1. Test the hardware interface independent of the program.

2. Test the operation of the entire system by running numerous problems where the answer is already known.

3. How does the program differentiate between positive and negative numbers?

Questions for Further Study

1. What precautions must be exercised when using this program?

2. Is there a way to permanently install this system in your microcomputer?

3. What must be added to allow the system to multiply two 4 character hexadecimal numbers?

Experiment 12

MICROPROCESSOR SOFTWARE

Purpose

In this experiment the student will be introduced to software and terminology. Particular emphasis will be on assembly language programming; however, compilers, interpreters, operating systems and editors will also be mentioned.

Background Investigation

Programs can take a variety of forms. In the digital computer area, programs can be a series of instructions written to perform a specified task. For an analog computer, a program may take the form of a wiring diagram used to specify the interconnection of a group of operational amplifiers. Devices such as timers can be programmed, and these are not even considered computers.

In order to write a program, one must be capable of performing the operation or task independent of the computer. The computer in effect must be told what to do in every case; it can only do it faster. Programmers must meet every eventuality with a reasonable response. Flowcharts are often used in planning for these eventualities and providing an organized plan of attack. To assist in an overall view of the problem, two flowcharts can be drawn. The first should be a general approach outlining the series of operations and decisions, in general terms, that must be performed. The second is a more specific flowchart depicting the details of individual algorithms to be programmed. In each case, however, blocks in the chart should be written in a clear concise form using words and standard mathematical notations. This relieves the creator from trying to remember instructions and allows one to concentrate on the problem. The flowchart is also independent of computer language allowing others to easily follow the procedure.

Machine language, the most fundamental computer language, is available on all computers, although the form of instructions may vary. Binary bit patterns form the basic instruction set. When learning to program a microprocessor, this is the most logical starting point. In addition, in the manufacturing process where it is important to conserve memory space, this is probably the most efficient method of programming.

Assembly language is similar to machine language with the exception

79

that the binary op codes are replaced with a mnemonic representation. Several advantages can be found over machine language programming.

1. Symbolic addresses are used rather than absolute addresses,

2. Mnemonic listings are easier to read,

3. Most assemblers allow for comments,

4. Additions and deletions of statements can be made easily without the need for reassignment of address or an excess number of NOPs,

5. Tedious tasks, such as decimal to binary conversions, may be handled with pseudo operators.

The one to one correspondence between assembly language and machine language still makes this an efficient means of programming.

Compilers are often used to translate higher level languages such as PL1, Fortran or Basic into machine language for later execution. The ease of programming in a higher level language is often offset by the fact that this translation results in a less efficient program, generating more machine language statements than necessary.

Interpreters are also popular on microprocessor systems. These programs are similar to compilers in that they convert a higher level language into instructions more easily understood by the processor, but they recompile each statement every time it is executed. These software systems are slow but require less memory space than their compiler counterparts.

Every system from the assembler to the compiler requires some means of entering and correcting the program from a keyboard. This is usually accomplished by the editor program. In some systems, the editor may be an integral part of the assembler or interpreter. The functions of the editor must be thoroughly understood if the programs are to be efficiently entered and debugged.

An operating system allows the user to control which programs are being executed and also to control system operation. On most micro-computer development systems, the master control program or executive (operating system) is an integral part of the operating system.

Prelaboratory Investigation

1. Draw a detailed flowchart on how to get to work or school in the morning. Start when leaving the front door and finish when you sit down at your desk.

The following questions pertain to the assembler used for this experiment.

2. Determine the correct mnemonics for each instruction available for the particular microprocessor used.

3. What means are used to enter data in an instruction, such as a load immediate instruction?

4. How many letters or letter/number combinations may be used in a symbolic address?

5. What is the correct format for entering an instruction into the assembler?

6. What pseudo operators are available?

7. Does the last statement in the assembly lising have to be END or STOP?

8. Should the first statement in the assembly listing define the starting address of the machine language output?

9. Is it necessary to assign a line number to each statement inputted?

10. How can an entire line be deleted?

11. How can individual characters be deleted while typing?

12. What does the term LABEL mean?

13. How may comments or remarks be entered?

14. Does the assembler have a permanent system symbol table? What for?

15. How can the values NO1 and NO2 in the above program be initialized through the assembler?

16. What types of error codes can be expected from the assembler?

17. Develop a memory map of available memory space showing the RAM areas set aside for:

    a) system use

    b) assembly listing

    c) symbol table

    d) machine language storage

18. Write a simple program in assembly language to add two numbers stored in memory at NO1 and NO2 and store the results in RES.

Laboratory Investigation

1. Assemble the program written in step 18 of the prelaboratory in-
    vestigation and verify proper execution.

2. Continue to use the assembler/editor and obtain first hand
    experience as to its operation and test your responses to
    the questions in the prelaboratory investigation.

Questions for Further Study

1. Compare the software systems discussed as to speed, memory space
    required and ease of use.

2. Define the following software terms:

    a) Microprogramming

    b) Simulator

    c) Translator

    d) Source code

    e) Object code

3. What is the history of the phrase "bug in the system/program"?

Experiment 13

BINARY MULTIPLICATION

Purpose

The purpose of this experiment is to develop technqiues for binary multiplication.

Background Investigation

Many microprocessors do not have a provision for hardware multiplication or division. It was not one of the primary considerations when the microprocessor was originally introduced. Intended to be used primarily for control applications, multiplication was initially considered to be one of the lesser important hardware functions. Most of the newer, 16 bit microprocessors do contain this provision. Most minicomputers also include a hardware multiply as standard, or at least an option.

The fact that a particular microprocessor/microcomputer does not have hardware multiply does not mean that it can't be done; it simply means that it is a job which must be relegated to software. Transducers, conversions and data manipulation may all require some form of multiplication to arrive at the desired result.

The number of bit positions required to store the answer in a multiplication procedure must be considered first. If two eight bit numbers are multiplied together, the result could possibly be as long as 16 bits. Therefore, in most cases, a double precision word is needed to store the result. Most of the examples treated in this experiment will assume there are two four bit numbers to be multiplied and the result will be an eight bit number. The procedures may be logically extended to include multiple precision values.

The simplest procedure for multiplying two numbers together is that of repeated addition. The procedure consists of adding the first number to itself as many times as the second number. This method may be slow, but it can be used successfully in nonspeed dependent applications. It is, however, extremely easy to program. The flowchart in figure 1 will illustrate this procedure. The flowchart will not work if either of the numbers are zero. This special case may be tested before the procedure is entered.

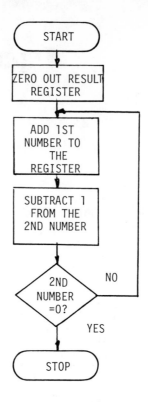

Figure 1: Repeated Addition Method

    A more speed efficient method may be employed that is slightly
more difficult to program. It is based on the same procedure as the
pencil and paper method. Consider for example

                27 multiplicand

                14 multiplier

The result may be found by forming two partial products: 4 x 27 and
10 x 27.

                27

                14

                108 (1st partial product 4x27)

                27   (2nd partial product 10x27)

                378 (sum of partial products)

The second partial product is shifted to the left one digit

84

position to reflect the factor of 10 in the multiplier position.

Binary multiplication may be conducted in a similar manner but no actual multiplication is ever performed. The multiplier in binary can only be one or zero. If it is one, the partial product is simply the same as the multiplicand; if it is zero, the partial product is also zero.

$$
\begin{array}{r}
1101 \\
1011 \\
\hline
\end{array}
$$

1101	1st partial product
1101	2nd partial product
0000	3rd partial product
1101	4th partial product
10001111	(sum of partial products)

Note the two initial numbers are only four bit but the result is an eight bit number. This is a shift and add procedure. The same partial product may be used over and over by simply shifting it to the left each time.

A flowchart of this process appears below in figure 2. In this flowchart, the multiplier will be stored in a four bit Y register, the multiplicand in an eight bit X register and the answer will be stored in an eight bit accumulator register A.

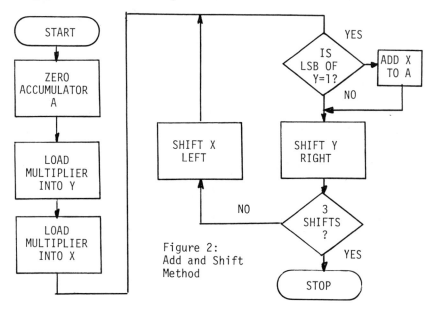

Figure 2:
Add and Shift
Method

85

The multiplication of signed numbers involves the same process as unsigned with the exception that the signs must be accounted for. The sign of the answer may be determined by checking the MSB of the multiplier and the multiplicand. Assuming that 0 is positive and 1 is negative, then:

$$0 \times 0 = 0$$

$$0 \times 1 = 1$$

$$1 \times 0 = 1$$

$$1 \times 1 = 0$$

This is simply an exclusive OR function. Once the sign of the result has been determined, either of the two numbers may be converted to their positive counterparts and the flowchart of figure 2 used.

It may not always be necessary to use a general purpose multiplication routine. If, for example, it is only necessary to multiply a number by 2, then the number can be simply shifted left one place. In fact, any time a multiplier is a power of 2, i.e., 2,4,8,16..., the multiplicand need only be shifted the appropriate number of places.

Other products can also be found using this same procedure, provided that the numbers can be broken down into a power of two and then simply added.

$$12(X) = 8(X) + 4(X)$$

$8(X)$ may be found by shifting X to the left 3 places and $4(X)$ can be found by shifting X 2 places left.

Prelaboratory Investigation

1. Write a multiplication routine which will multiply two eight bit signed numbers and form a 16 bit signed result.

2. When signed numbers are used, one case $(-128_{10} \times -128_{10})$ will not work with the procedure as described in the background investigation. Why?

3. Devise a procedure for:

$$(X)(60_{10})$$

Laboratory Investigation

1. Verify the correct operation of the general multiplication routine.

2. What special provisions does your program have to handle cases

such as

$$0(X) \text{ and,}$$

$$-128_{10}(X)?$$

3. Verify the accurate calculation of

$$(X)(60_{10}).$$

4. What is the largest value that X can be in step 3 above if the result is to fit in an eight bit unsigned register?

Questions for Further Study

1. What does the generalized add and shift technique have in common with the procedure used to multiply X times 60_{10}?

2. List three procedures that may be used to divide two binary numbers.

3. What are the limitations of each method in item 2 above?

4. Investigate how a hardware multiplication method works. How is it similar to or different from the software methods previously discussed?

ALGORITHMIC DEVELOPMENT - FINDING THE SQUARE ROOT

Purpose

The purpose of this experiment is to investigate the development of an algorithm. Specifically, a program will be written to find the square root of an integer number.

Background Investigation

Applications of a microprocessor to system control involves the interface to various transducers. The output of a transducer is subsequently "read" by the microprocessor for further processing or decision making. A group of transducers exhibit a similar property whereby their output is a function of the square of the input. These square law devices may be characterized by the following equation:

$$y = kx^2$$

where k represents a constant of proportionality.

An example to illustrate this concept may be taken from fluid power. Transducers are available which will produce an output voltage proportional to pressure in a system. Measurement of flow, however, is not so easily accomplished. It can be shown that pressure is proportional to the square of the flow through an orifice. Using a pressure transducer, flow can therefore be determined by the following:

$$f = k\sqrt{v}$$

Thus the importance for the study of the square root procedure may be seen in light of subsequent investigations involving similar devices.

Many procedures have been developed to determine the square root of an integer number. These procedures all arrive at the same answer but vary considerably in the number of steps. However, all have a common characteristic; they comprise what is known as an algorithm. An algorithm may be defined as a set of unambiguous statements specifying an order of operations that provides the solution to a specific class of problems. The lack of ambiguity tends to insure the algorithm will be easily adaptable to a program. All options, special considerations and eventualities must have predetermined options. The order of operations should be well defined. In fact, one method for displaying the order of operations would be a flowchart. The final procedure should solve the entire class of problems, i.e., all integer square roots, all roots of polynomials, all inverse matrices, etc.

Many people have forgotten the method used to find the square root that was originally taught in school. Perhaps the advent of the electronic calculator or the lack of repeated use has caused this. This method may be illustrated by an example. To determine the square root of 841, the numbers must be first separated in two digit groups beginning at the decimal point. The remaining steps in this procedure

$$\sqrt{8\ \underline{41}}$$

may be listed as follows:

1. Determine a digit whose square is as close as possible to 8 but not larger.
2. Subtract the square of this number from 8 and bring down the next two digits.

$$\begin{array}{r} 2 \\ \sqrt{8\ 41} \\ 4 \\ \hline 4\ 41 \end{array}$$

3. Next, a trial divisor must be determined by doubling the 2 and determining a digit x such that when it is multiplied by the trial divisor the result will be less than or equal to 441, $[x(4x) \leq 441]$.

$$\begin{array}{r} 2\ x \\ \sqrt{8\ 41} \\ 4 \\ \hline 4x/4\ 41 \end{array}$$

4. In this case, x = 9, and result, 29, is the square root of 841.

Note that the equation in step 3 above, if it were to be solved by normal means, would itself require a square root algorithm. The trial and error approach seems to circumvent this problem. All in all, this procedure does involve some guess work (step 3) and would not easily be adaptable to the computer.

Another technique, based on the Newton-Raphson method, employs the following formula:

$$y_{i+1} = y_i + \frac{1}{2}\left(\frac{a}{y_i} - y_i\right)$$

This iterative method is based on the initial guess y_1 and with each iteration, becomes closer and closer to the desired root. Unfortunately, this method is easy to program in a higher level language such as FORTRAN or BASIC but is not easily adaptable to machine or assembly language due to the floating point operations involved.

The algorithm that will be employed for this experiment is easy to program in machine language and works equally well in any number base. It is based on the fact that any perfect square can be determined by counting the number of odd terms that add to equal the perfect square.

Odd Terms	Perfect Square	Number of Terms
1	1	1
1+3	4	2
1+3+5	9	3
1+3+5+7	16	4
1+3+5+7+9	25	5

Note that in every case above, the number of odd terms in the series is equal to the square root. This process may be programmed by continual subtracting of the odd terms beginning with 1 until the next digit cannot be subtracted without producing a negative sum.

$$
\begin{array}{r}
36 \\
-\ 1 \\
\hline
35 \\
-\ 3 \\
\hline
32 \\
-\ 5 \\
\hline
27 \\
-\ 7 \\
\hline
20 \\
-\ 9 \\
\hline
11 \\
-11 \\
\hline
0
\end{array}
\Bigg\} \quad 7 \text{ subtractions}
$$

Even the square roots of numbers which are not perfect squares may be determined using this procedure by shifting the decimal point to the right two places at a time until the desired accuracy is achieved. If, for example, the square root of 34 is to be determined, and the number is changed to 3400, an additional digit of accuracy may be found. In this case 58 subtractions would be performed resulting in an answer of 5.8.

Prelaboratory Investigation

1. A simple procedure may be developed to determine the integer value closest to the square root of the number in question. Develop this procedure.

2. Using the subtractive process and the procedure developed in step 1 above, draw a complete step by step flowchart for this procedure.

3. Code the solution using memory locations for the square and square root results.

4. Develop a procedure to make this entire program a subroutine for use in subsequent programs.

Laboratory Investigation

1. Observe the correct operation of your program by attempting to determine the square root of a minimum of three example problems.

2. Write a main program for the square root subroutine written in step 4 of the Prelaboratory Investigation and again verify the correct operation of this program.

3. What provision exists in your program to handle negative numbers?

Questions for Further Study

1. Large numbers require a lengthy subtraction process and may require too much computer time for specific applications. Either through investigation of literature or by development, determine a technique based on the subtraction process which can be used to considerably shorten the execution time of this program.

2. Classify each of the three methods outlined in the Background section with respect to computer time to execute and length of program required.

3. Using either a high level language or a pocket calculator, determine the number of iterations required in the Newton-Raphson based method to determine the square root of 3400. Compare this to the subtraction method.

Experiment 15

ARRAYS AND TABLES

Purpose

The various aspects of arrays and tables as well as specific applications in algorithmic development will be covered in this experiment.

Background Investigation

Methods of storing similar and related values in a microcomputer program vary widely and are not as obviously simple as it may first appear. Methods of arranging this data in an ordered fashion can significantly reduce program size and execution times. Examples of the use of arrays can be recalled from matrix algebra and high level programs where storage areas may be reserved by dimension statements. Before the introduction of the calculator, tables were often used to determine values of sine, cosine and logarithmic functions. Tables and arrays find a variety of uses in the microcomputer applications as well, such as moving blocks of data/instructions, sorting, conversion of one form of data to another, data storage and retrieval, etc.

A group of values stored in a block of consecutive memory locations that have a definite relationship may be referenced as an array or table. The differences between the array and the table result primarily from the subsequent application. When a mathematical operation is to be performed that will either generate or alter this group of values, the term array is most often used. If the values are stored simply for further reference, the term table-look-up is most often used. The list below shows some typical applications of both of these terms.

Arrays	Tables
Moving blocks of data	Binary to seven segment conversion
Searching for a specific value	Centigrade to Fahrenheit conversion
Determining maximum & minimum	Sine, cosine determination
Sorting	Code conversions

Tables are most often used where there is no simple mathematical formula available to do the conversions. In the list above, a mathematical formula for converting an input binary number to seven segment codes cannot easily be determined. A program would be significantly shorter if these values were simply determined from an accompanying table. In the microcomputer software, tables may be used to avoid lengthy multiplication and division routines.

Before a table or an array can be used, a group of memory locations must be reserved for storing these values. Care should be exercised in making this reservation because, as will be discussed later, address information can often be used cleverly as part of the look-up process. In higher level languages such as Fortran, a DIMENSION statement may be used to define the maximum size of the array. In assembly language, statements such as the ones listed below may be used.

LBL   RES   40H

LBL   DS   40H

In both cases above, LBL represents the symbolic address of the first location in the array or table and 40H specifies the size as 40 hexadecimal locations. The pseudo op codes RES and DS stand for re-serve and define segment, respectively, and may vary from assembler to assembler. If an assembler is not used, and coding is done directly in machine language, then care should be taken to insure that the storage area is not invaded by program instructions. In either case, a memory map should be drawn indicating the area set aside for instructions, I/O and data storage. This master plan will insure the most efficient use of memory. In cases where data in a table is always constant and is not changed by program action, it may be stored in ROM or PROM so that it does not have to be redefined on every power up.

Modes of addressing become more influential when arrays and tables are used. Indirect addressing methods find great utility in referencing positions within these arrays. A base address, the address of the first location in the array, may be loaded into a register. Subsequent references to sequential memory locations may be made by simply incrementing this register and using the contents as an address.

A search routine may be developed to find the address of a specific data value stored in a block of memory. This block of memory would become an array or table and may be defined as such by the techniques previously discussed. A flowchart for this procedure appears below.

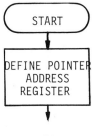

START

DEFINE POINTER
ADDRESS
REGISTER

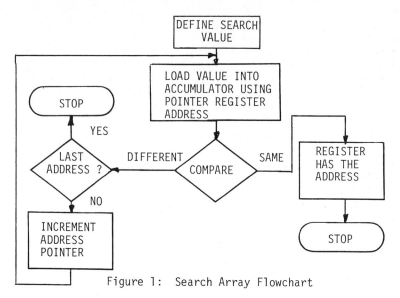

Figure 1: Search Array Flowchart

    The concept of two dimensional arrays may be handled in the
microcomputer software even though the memory is thought of as being
a single dimension. A block of memory may be defined as shown in
figure 2. A block number is specified as one dimension and then a relative location within the block becomes the second.

Block 1   Block 2

1 ____   1 ____

2 ____   2 ____

3 ____   3 ____

Figure 2: Double
Array Referencing   4 ____   4 ____

                           .   .
                           .   .
                           .   .

Block 3   ...   Block n

1 ____   1 ____

2 ____   2 ____

3 ____   3 ____

4 ____   4 ____

.   .
.   .
.   .

94

These blocks are placed end to end and are stored sequentially in memory. The length of each block must be previously defined and adhered to. Of course, fewer locations than specified may be in use at any given time.

It is often necessary in file management to move one block of data from one location to another. This may be accomplished by using two pointer registers for addressing. If the particular microprocessor being used does not provide for two indirect addressing registers to be used simultaneously then other means must be employed. The flowchart in figure 3 shows a general procedure that may be followed in moving blocks of data.

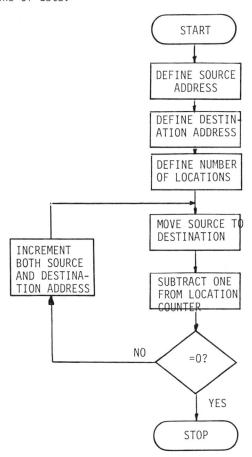

Figure 3: Data Transfer Routine

This routine may also be used to move a program provided that all transfer statements are of the relative branch type where no absolute locations are referenced. If the program contains transfer instructions of the absolute type, a check could be performed to locate all transfer instructions and a bias address may be added or subtracted from the address specified. This would allow machine language programs to be relocated, a great advantage.

Sorting is another often used procedure that operates on and transforms an array of values. In addition to numeric sorting, alphanumeric sorts are also performed. In the latter case, characters are usually stored in memory in ASCII format. This becomes a seven or eight bit representation of the letter. Because the values in ASCII code are in numerical order when they are in alphabetical order, the same procedure may be applied to both.

A commonly used sorting technique is based on the procedure outlined in figure 4. This technique, known as a bubble sort, uses a sequence of comparisons to arrive at the final value. During the first pass, the first number in the list is assumed to be the smallest (if the final list is to be in ascending order). Each of the remaining numbers in the list is then compared. Every time a smaller value is found, it is swapped with the first value. On the second pass, the second number in the list is assumed to be the smallest and subsequently all values below this number are compared for a possible swap. The procedure continues until the last value in the list is encountered.

PASS 1

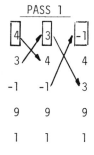

PASS 2

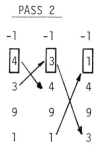

PASS 3

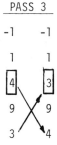

PASS 4

Figure 4:   Bubble
Sorting Example
Problem

Tables are often employed to store data when no simple mathematical formula to describe the interrelationships exists. A typical example of the use of a table can be drawn from the optical seven segment displays. If it is desired to perform the binary to seven segment decoding, normally done by an integrated circuit such as a 7447 or 7448, using software and the I/O ports of the microcomputer, a table look-up procedure would most likely be employed. Obviously, no simple mathematical relationship exists to perform this conversion. A table of conversion values appears in figure 5. The binary value (BCD in this case) appears as an address for the row of values which may be stored in memory. If the first ten locations in memory are reserved to store the seven bits (segment) information, then the inputted binary value may be used directly as an address. In other circumstances a base address of any value may be used and the inputted binary code simply be added to the base value.

```
        a
    f  ___  b
       |   |
        g
    e  ___  c
       |   |
       ___
        d
```

Binary Input	Segment Code						
	a	b	c	d	e	f	g
0 0 0 0	1	1	1	1	1	1	0
0 0 0 1	0	1	1	0	0	0	0
0 0 1 0	1	1	0	1	1	0	1
0 0 1 1	1	1	1	1	0	0	1
0 1 0 0	0	1	1	0	0	1	1
0 1 0 1	1	0	1	1	0	1	1
0 1 1 0	0	0	1	1	1	1	1
0 1 1 1	1	1	1	0	0	0	0
1 0 0 0	1	1	1	1	1	1	1
1 0 0 1	1	1	1	0	0	1	1

Figure 5: Binary to Seven Segment Conversion Table

The input data is used to address the desired entry in the table in figure 5. The base address would contain the desired data for the "0" display, base plus one for the "1", base plus two for the "2" and so on. The key factor for a fast look-up is that there is no table search conducted because the input data becomes the address of the correct entry.

Another example of the table look-up approach is the conversion of degrees centigrade to degrees Fahrenheit. The formula for this conversion is:

$$°C = 5/9 \ (°F-32)$$

The use of the formula directly would involve a subtraction followed by a multiplication. In some applications the resolution required may be to only one degree C. The time required to perform this conversion may be too lengthy. A look-up table may be used to speed up this conversion process. A table of 180 entries may be constructed such that the temperature in °F may be used to reference the proper value. Locations would be represented in hexadecimal notation and the corresponding temperature may be represented in BCD, if we assume the temperature range to be from 0 to 99°C. A portion of the table appears in figure 6. A similar table may be developed for conversion to degrees Fahrenheit.

HEX Address	BCD Contents	Remarks
20	00	32°F = 0°C
21	01	33°F = 1°C
22	01	34°F = 1°C
.	.	.
.	.	.
.	.	.
26	04	40°F = 4°C
.	.	.
.	.	.
.	.	.
	99	210°F = 99°C

Figure 6:   °C to °F Conversion

A table look-up may also be employed to determine the sine of an angle. Depending on the sophistication of the procedure, the table may contain 90, 180 or 360 entries. Actually the table need only contain 90 entries. Angles greater than 90 degrees may be reduced to an angle between 0 and 90 if care is taken to remember the appropriate sign.

Prelaboratory Investigation

1. Write a program which will clear a block of memory. The block may have any starting address and be of any length up to 16 k.

2. Devise a program which will determine the minimum and maximum of an array of sign two's complement numbers.

3. Code the program for the bubble sort procedure as discussed in the background investigation.

4. Devise a program to convert °C to °F. Assume that only BCD values of °C between 0 and 99 will be entered.

5. Write a checksum program which will use the exclusive OR operation.

Laboratory Investigation

1. Test the min-max program written in step 1 of the prelaboratory investigation with all possible values. Be sure all possible range of negative as well as positive numbers are used.

2. Using the bubble sort routine previously developed, sort in ascending order at least 200 words of memory.

3. Investigate the operation of the °C to °F conversion routine. Do you present the output °F temperature in base 10 or binary?

4. Using the checksum program, determine the checksum of a block of memory containing random data. Change one bit in the data block and compare the results. Repeat for a two bit and three bit change.

5. How may the program of step 4 be changed to perform an AND, OR or NOR operation instead of an exclusive OR?

Questions for Further Study

1. A table look-up scheme may be devised using the stack pointer as the indicator for the address of the proper entry. Draw a flow-chart to convert binary to the seven segment code using the stack.

2. Determine, in general terms, the number of comparisons that must be made in a bubble sorting routine.

3. The sine table look-up procedure previously discussed may be modified to shorten the length of the table from 90 entries. Assume entries are present for every four degrees instead of every degree. Develop a procedure to interpolate angles not given in the table.

Experiment 16

DECISION MAKING PROCESS

Purpose

Various aspects of the decision making process will be studied as applied to intelligent computer games in this experiment.

Background Investigation

Computerized games are often simply a fad for the user. When quickly mastered, they often become disgarded for the next wave. The more intelligent the game and the more options employed tend to make its captivation longer lasting. The abundance of these applications on the market today often leads one to believe that the major market is in the home entertainment area.

The approach to developing a computer game involves a well thought-out plan that often involves relying on past experiences and adaptive methodologies. For the programmer, it is an experience which may prove invaluable in industrial control and other applications. The true utility of an intelligent device is the ability to make appropriate decisions based on input data and act in a predescribed manner.

Various microcomputer applications have been introduced in recent years that "play" games such as football, basketball, magic square, blackjack and even chess. The ability of these systems to hold the interest of the user is based on its ability to provide an appropriate level of challenge. In this experiment one such game will be studied, i.e., tic-tac-toe or noughts and crosses as it is called in other parts of the world.

This two player game's objectives are well known to most and will not be discussed at this point. An algorithm can be developed by forming a mathematical relationship based on a weighted value assigned to each of nine possible locations. This procedure is quite straightforward and very well defined. So well defined, in fact, that the computer will never lose. It may not always win, but in the worst case it would be a draw.

The game board is numbered as shown in figure 1. The numbering is critical due to the mathematical relationships soon to be presented.

```
 1 │ 2 │ 3
───┼───┼───
 8 │ 9 │ 4
───┼───┼───
 7 │ 6 │ 5
```

Figure 1: The Game Board

The computer moves will be assigned A-B-C-D-E for the first, second, ... moves, respectively. The player moves will be assigned the characters P-Q-R-S. For the most advantageous situation for the computer, it will always move first and will go the middle. The following sequence of steps will show the proper response for inputted moves.

In all cases where the computer moves are calculated in the following steps, if the resulting numerical value is greater than eight, then eight must be subtracted to obtain the proper move.

1. Computer moves A=9,

2. Player moves P,

3. Calculate computer move B=P+1 (if B > 8 then B=B-8),

4. Player moves Q,

5. If Q is not equal to B+4 then C=B+4 and the computer wins, otherwise C=B+2,

6. Player moves R,

7. If R is not equal to C+4 then D=C+4 and the game is a draw, otherwise if P was odd then C=C+7 and the computer wins, if P was even, D=C+3,

8. Player moves S,

9. If S is not equal to D+4 then the computer moves E=D+4 and the computer wins, otherwise E=D+6 and the result is a draw.

This procedure will always result in at least a draw. It should again be noted that any time the computer move calculation results in a number greater than eight, then eight must be subtracted to give an appropriate answer. There are several disadvantages in using this procedure. First, the computer always goes first. Second, using the same player moves, the computer will always respond with identical moves, making the game less interesting for more than a couple of games. Third, the computer never lets anyone win, causing frustration at best.

If another procedure is employed, it should allow the player the ·

first move. This would significantly increase the interest in the game. In addition, an adaptive program would allow the player to win until the program "learned" the procedures. The program would then begin winning consistently.

Another common game found in the program library of most computer systems is the game of NIM. This game is based on the following procedure:

1. A number is chosen at random,

2. Each player is requested to subtract a number from the original sum in turn,

3. At least one must be subtracted but no more than the maximum value stated,

4. The last player to subtract a number wins.

To better understand this process, a decision tree of all possible combinations is shown in figure 2. This is based on a game with an initial number of five and a maximum subtraction of two.

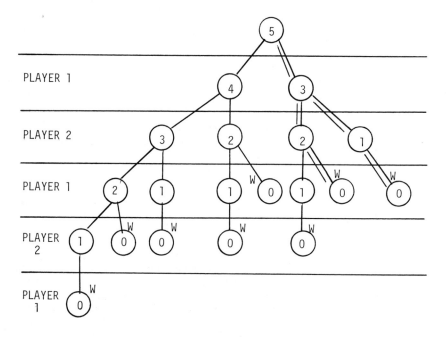

Figure 2: Decision Tree

The graph shows all possible paths to reach zero. In each case, a win
is registered for the player who performs the last subtraction. Obviously, the only player that can insure a win is player 1 due to the
structure of the tree. Player 1 can direct the process to flow along
the double lines shown by subtracting two on the initial play. Regardless of the subtraction of player 2, player 1 can obtain a win with
the last move. The flow of the game is never allowed to follow the
left path since either player may win.

In both of the games discussed, the process of selecting the
appropriate decisions is a complex one. In the tic-tac-toe procedure
outlined, a system of calculations and tests may be performed to insure a win. This process may become lengthy and require a vast
amount of storage to contain the program. The decision tree approach,
on the other hand, would be considerably more compact for larger
systems.

In general, a graph is composed of nodes (connecting points) and
branches between the nodes. Each node may be uniquely numbered beginning with zero. Likewise, each branch would have its own assigned
reference value. Several graphs are shown below.

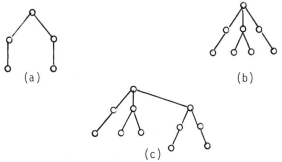

(a)   (b)

(c)

Figure 3: Graphs

The unique feature about the graph shown in figure 3(a) is that
it contains a loop or closed path while the graphs in figure 3(b) and
(c) do not. The two graphs in (b) and (c) are referred to as trees
because they have branches which connect every node but have no loops.
Every decision tree has branches which connect the nodes but have no
loops. An entire study of graphs and associated pnemonima is referred
to as topology.

Methods of storing these graphs in memory vary widely. One procedure is based on an array or matrix of the graph called an incidence
matrix. Rows in the matrix correspond to nodes and columns correspond
to branches. A graph and its incidence matrix are shown in Figure 4.
Note that the row shows all the branches incident on a node. Each
column has only two entries, one for each end point of the branch.

103

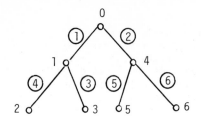

BRANCHES

		1	2	3	4	5	6
N	0	1	1	0	0	0	0
O	1	1	0	1	1	0	0
D	2	0	0	0	1	0	0
E	3	0	0	1	0	0	0
S	4	0	1	0	0	1	1
	5	0	0	0	0	1	0
	6	0	0	0	0	0	1

Figure 4: The Incidence Matrix

An array of this type may be stored in sequential memory locations with addresses corresponding to node numbers as long as the number of branches does not exceed the word length of the machine. (The number of branches in any decision tree is always the number of nodes -1.) Multiple precision words may be used for larger graphs.

Other methods may be employed to store this information by creating arrays that contain the node and branch information as shown. These are all essentially similar.

Branches			Node End Points		
Node	0-1,2		Branch	1	1,0
	1-1,3,4			2	0,4
	2-4			3	1,3
	3-3			4	1,2
	4-2,5,6			5	4,5
	5-5			6	4,6
	6-6				

Each of these methods have advantages and disadvantages based on a particular application. Reference points within these arrays may be made based on a cross-reference array designed especially for this purpose. Only necessary paths need be stored in an array of this type. Referring to the tree in figure 2, the right path is the only critical one and the left path will never be taken if the program is properly written.

Prelaboratory Analysis

1. Draw a decision tree for the tic-tac-toe procedure outlined in the background investigation.

2. Flowchart the first method for tic-tac-toe discussed in the background investigation.

3. Program the procedure.

4. Develop a decision tree for the game of NIM for an initial number of 7 with a maximum subtraction value of 4. Only those branches which will result in a win for player 1 need be shown.

5. Program the game as outlined in step 4 above.

6. Can a general procedure be developed to use any initial starting number for NIM such that player 1 will always win?

Laboratory Investigation

1. Test the tic-tac-toe program developed in step 3 of the prelaboratory analysis by attempting all possible combinations of moves.

2. Verify the correct operation of the NIM game program of step 5.

Questions for Further Study

1. Construct a decision tree showing the first three moves of the tic-tac-toe game. This should include all possibilities. Note the symmetry may be employed to significantly reduce the problem. Can you project the number of different possible games that exist?

2. Develop a procedure to play the Os in the tic-tac-toe game. This procedure could be employed to enable one computer to play another.

3. List possible applications where a decision tree may be employed. What are the general characteristics of such applications?

4. Draw a tree showing the chain of command in the Army beginning with the general. Is this type of tree called a binary tree? Why or why not?

Experiment 17

STACK OPERATIONS

Purpose

The purpose of this experiment is to investigate the operation and use of the stack for data storage and manipulation.

Background Investigation

The stack is a read/write area typically located in the user RAM area; however, in some of the early microprocessors, this area was located within the microprocessor itself. The stack is typically a last-in-first-out (LIFO) arrangement. The last piece of data to be stored on the stack is the first one that can be retrieved. Other computer systems may have FIFO, FILO or LILO protocols, but microprocessors are almost exclusively LIFO.

The location of the stack in RAM is determined by an internal register called the stack pointer. In an eight bit processor, this is usually a 16 bit address register. It points to the current location of the stack. Two pointer methods are used.

1. The pointer will indicate the next empty location available for stack data transfer, or

2. The pointer will indicate the last data word that has been transferred.

The stack pointer location must typically be initialized when power is first applied to the microprocessor due to the fact that this address register reacts like RAM. If the initialization step is omitted, the stack may be placed in a location that does not contain memory and all data transferred there may be lost. Load stack pointer and load register pair immediate are instructions that may accomplish this initialization step.

Whenever data is transferred to the stack, the pointer register is decremented. In other words, the data fills the high order address locations first. The stack pointer is always decremented by the number of words placed on the stack. When data is taken from the stack, the pointer is incremented by the appropriate number of locations. (Actually, when data is taken from the stack, only the pointer changes and the original data placed on the stack remains in RAM.)

106

Data may be placed onto the stack by a Push instruction or transferred back to the CPU by a Pull or Pop instruction. A stack in RAM may appear as given below. The data in RAM above the pointer is either the remains of prior stack pulls or random power up bit configurations, but in either case do not affect the stack.

Address	Contents
OFFA	47
OFFB	40
OFFC	00
OFFD	10
OFFE	DE
OFFF	FC
SP → 1000	NO RAM AVAILABLE HERE

In the example given above, the stack pointer has been initialized at a location one greater than the RAM area available. This is the procedure that would be followed, in a processor such as the 8080, where the pointer indicates the location of the last data that was deposited.

If the bytes 00 and 01 were pushed onto the stack, it would appear as

	OFFA	47
	OFFB	40
	OFFC	00
	OFFD	10
SP →	OFFE	01
	OFFF	00
	1000	

When the additional bytes, 05 and FF, were pushed onto the stack, it would appear as

	OFFA	47
	OFFB	40
SP →	OFFC	FF

107

OFFD	05
OFFE	01
OFFF	00
1000	

If these bytes were pulled or popped from the stack back to the CPU, the stack area would remain unchanged, but the pointer would be incremented back to 1000.

The stack is designed to fill memory beginning at the high order address. Programs, on the other hand, typically begin at low order addresses, thus more efficient use of memory may be made. Care should be taken so the two areas do not overlap.

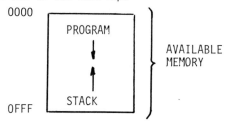

Figure 1: Memory Management

The stack has three primary functions in a microprocessor development system.

1. Subroutine CALL. When a subroutine is called by a main program, the address of the next location in memory is automatically saved on the stack.

2. Interrupts. When the processor receives a request for interrupt, the address of the next location to be executed, when the interrupt is finished, is saved on the stack before the program control branches to the service routine.

3. Saving data and the CPU's internal registers. The internal data stored in the processor can be "saved" on the stack so that they may be freed for other uses; when the procedure has been finished, the registers may be restored from the stack. (In some microprocessor units, the internal registers are automatically saved following an operation like an interrupt.)

When a subroutine is called, for example:

1. The contents of the program counter will be saved on the stack.

2. The first few statements of the subroutine may, if the programmer desires, save internal registers on the stack.

3. The remainder of the subroutine is executed.

4. Before the return is executed, the internal registers are restored.

5. The RETURN statement reestablishes the program counter, from the stack, with the next location to be executed in the calling program.

Upon the completion of the above steps, the stack pointer will be exactly at the same location it was before the subroutine was called. It must be, by nature of the LIFO stack operation, that whatever is placed onto the stack, by the subroutine, must be removed in reverse order before the RETURN is executed.

Other applications may also be developed to assist in the manipulation of data. The stack may become another addressing mode that will allow programs to be written considerably shorter. One register pair (on the 8085) may be interchanged with another register pair by pushing the data onto the stack and popping it back in the new location. The order of data stored in memory may be reversed using stack commands. The stack provides a useful tool in the development of software and should be fully utilized.

Prelaboratory Investigation

1. Investigate the characteristics of the stack used by your microprocessor.

   a) How can the stack pointer be initialized?

   b) Where does the register point, to the last data deposited or to the next available location?

   c) What instructions affect the contents of the stack? (List all including CALLS, interrupts, etc.)

2. How are the flags (carry, sign, parity, etc.) saved onto the stack?

3. Is it necessary for the stack to occupy the same RAM area as used by the processor? Why or why not?

4. Write a series of statements which will save the contents of the stack pointer for later use.

5. Outline the procedure for the use of the stack when using the interrupt procedure.

6. Write a program to add a list of 20 input numbers that have been stored in memory utilizing the stack pointer.

Laboratory Investigation

1. Test the characteristics of the stack pointer when a CALL to subroutine statement is encountered.

2. Test the statements written in step 4 of the prelaboratory investigation.

3. Verify the correct operation of the program from step 6 of the prelaboratory investigation.

Questions for Further Study

1. List at least two uses of the stack not mentioned in this experiment.

2. Why is it necessary to change the location of the stack pointer during the execution of a program?

3. What happens to the stack if a subroutine calls another subroutine?

4. What limits the number of levels of subroutine CALLS?

Experiment 18

DECIMAL TO BINARY AND BINARY TO DECIMAL CONVERSIONS

Purpose

In this experiment two algorithms will be presented to perform decimal to binary and binary to decimal conversions.

Background Investigation

Recall that base ten numbers can be written using positional notation where each position proceeding to the left from the decimal point is an increasing power of ten. Each position to the right would be a decreasing power of ten. In the number 129_{10}, three powers of ten are present: 10^0, 10^1 and 10^2. In positional notation, the number becomes:

$$129_{10} = 1 \times 10^2 + 2 \times 10^1 + 9 \times 10^0$$

In the above equation, the right side may be converted into binary values and summed. The result will be the binary equivalent of 129_{10}. Note that the multipliers 1, 2 and 9 can be easily converted to binary as follows:

$$1 = 0001$$

$$2 = 0010$$

$$9 = 1001$$

In fact, if the numbers 1, 2 and 9 are stored in individual memory locations, they would already be in this form. If they are expressed in BCD or if they are stored in ASCII, it would be a simple matter to store them in individual memory locations. The powers of ten can also be easily converted to binary as follows:

$$10^0 = 1 = 0001$$

$$10^1 = 10 = 1010$$

$$10^2 = 100 = (1010)^2$$

The conversion process therefore reduces to:

$$129_{10} = (0001)(1010)^2 + (0010)(1010) + (1001)(0001)$$

Two problems still remain. The first is the determination of 10^2. If one recalls one of the simpler procedures from algebra, the equation can be written as:

$$129_{10} = 1 \times 10^2 + 2 \times 10^1 + 9$$
$$= ((1)\ 10 + 2)\ 10 + 9$$

thus eliminating the need to raise numbers to a power.

$$129_{10} = ((0001)\ (1010) + 0010)\ 1010 + 1001$$

The second problem area is the necessity to multiply by 10. Multiplication is typically a difficult or time consuming process with a microprocessor. However, since all multiplications will be of the form

$$X\ (10) = X\ (1010)$$

then the process can be somewhat simplified.

Multiplication by 10 can be accomplished by multiplication by 2 (one rotate left) and adding 8 (three rotate lefts). The following example will illustrate this principle:

$$(2 \times 10_{10}) = 20_{10} = (0010)(1010)_2$$
$$= (0010)(0010) + (0010)(1000)$$
$$= 0100 + 1\ 0000$$
$$= 1\ 0100$$

In the previous example, therefore $129_{10} = (1 \times 10 + 2)\ 10 + 9$

$$129_{10} = ((0001)(1010) + 0010)\ 1010 + 1001$$

```
  0001   (base value)

  0010   (1 rotate)

+ 1000   (three rotates)

  1010   results in $(1 \times 10)_{10}$

+ 0010

  1100   results in $((1 \times 10) + 2)_{10}$

 11000   (one rotate)

+ 1100000   (three rotates)

1111000   results in $((1 \times 10) + 2)10_{10}$

+   1001   final value of 9 is added

100000001   $[((1 \times 10) + 2)10 + 9]_{10}$
```

A simple algorithm using only rotate and add instructions may be developed for this process and is shown in the flowcharts of figure 1 and 2.

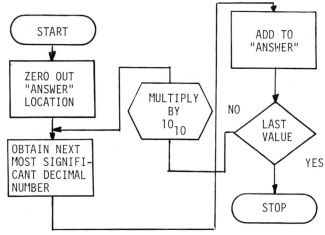

Figure 1: Decimal to Binary Conversion Routine

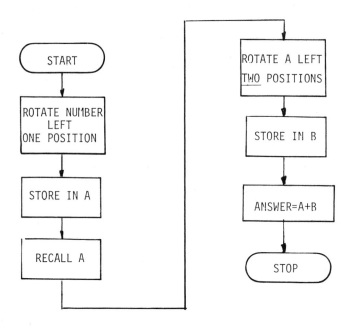

Figure 2: Procedure for Multiplying by 10_{10} or $(1010)_2$

Another procedure may be developed to convert binary to decimal. It is based on the following procedure. To convert 10000001_2 to base 10, the divisions will be performed as follows:

$$\frac{10000001 \; (129_{10})}{1010 \quad (10_{10})} = 1100 \text{ with a remainder of } 1001$$

$$\frac{1100}{1010} = 0001 \text{ with a remainder of } 0010$$

$$\frac{0001}{1010} = 0000 \text{ with a remainder of } 0001$$

The remainders 1001, 0010, 0001 form the base ten equivalent and may be stored in individual memory locations for subsequent conversion to ASCII or packed BCD. The first remainder is the least significant digit while the last remainder is the most significant digit. Hence:

$$0001 = 1$$
$$0010 = 2 \quad = \quad 129_{10}$$
$$1001 = 9$$

The division process may be accomplished by the repeated subtraction technique. For example, to divide 10000001 by 1010, simply subtract 1010 from 10000001 until a remainder less than 1010 is obtained. The number of subtractions is the answer.

Prelaboratory Investigation

1. Construct a subroutine for the procedure outlined in the flowcharts shown in figures 1 and 2 to convert any base ten number into binary. Write the program so that only positive integer numbers will be converted that are less than 225_{10}.

2. How can the procedure outlined above be modified to work with both positive and negative numbers? Note, the range of values will be -128 to +127 for an eight bit binary output.

3. Using a double precision notation for subsequent binary storage, what would be the range of positive and negative integer numbers that can be converted?

4. Develop a flowchart for the binary to decimal conversion routine described in the background investigation.

5. Code the flowchart from step 4 into a machine language subroutine. Use unsigned binary numbers less than eight bits in length.

6. Modify the procedure from step 5 above to output signed eight bit values.

7. If a keyboard is available for input and a printer or monitor for output, incorporate the signed decimal input and output routines written above into a simple base 10 addition main line program. The output should appear similar to the following:

$$12 + 14 = 26$$

where the 12 and 14 are entered from the keyboard.

Laboratory Investigation

1. Develop a series of test values that may be used in debugging the routines written in the prelaboratory investigation. These values should test all possible paths and special cases for the routines.

2. Verify the correct operation of the signed and unsigned decimal to binary conversion routines. (A short main program should be written to load three decimal values into consecutive memory locations, and call the subroutine. The binary answer should appear in the accumulator.)

3. Test the correct operation of the signed and unsigned binary to decimal conversion subroutine. (A main program should be written to place a binary value into the accumulator and call the subroutine. The decimal answer should appear in three consecutive memory locations.)

4. Test for the correct operation of the decimal addition program written in step 7 of the prelaboratory investigation.

Questions for Further Study

1. Why are the decimal to binary or binary to decimal conversion routines important?

2. How can a procedure be developed to perform binary to decimal conversion using the decimal adjust accumulator instruction? Can this instruction also be used to perform a decimal to binary conversion?

3. Using the procedures discussed in this experiment, show how the following number may be converted into binary.

128.34

What problems does a procedure such as this present?

4. Show how

10101100.0101110

may be converted into base ten. Are there any special cases that deserve further investigation?

5. How could the decimal portions of the binary numbers in questions 3 and 4 above be stored internally?

Experiment 19

SEVEN SEGMENT DISPLAYS AND MULTIPLEXING

Purpose

The purpose of this experiment is to investigate the use of seven segment displays, decoder drivers and latches in various configurations in microprocessor applications.

Background Investigation

LED displays used in most digital applications are of the seven segment variety. These displays may be either common anode or common cathode and may vary to suit some special requirement. The 7447 and 7448 ICs are normally used as decoder/drivers for common anode and common cathode, respectively, for BCD representation. These devices will produce digits 0-9 for the appropriate binary input. For binary inputs greater than 9, 7447 and 7448 produce outputs, but are not easily recognizable.

Devices such as the 9368, 9369 and 9370 produce readable outputs for inputs 0-15 and display higher values (10-15) in the hexadecimal format. For the purposes of this experiment, the inputs to these devices, normally given the symbols ABCD, will be assumed to correspond to the binary input where D is the MSB and A is the LSB.

The output representation for the hexadecimal display is not always easily readable and, at times, may require careful interpretation. In figure 1 it can be seen that the values for b and 6 can be easily confused. The critical nature of some segments can also be noted from the figure. If the middle segment is burned out, an eight could be interpreted as a zero. In many applications a lamp test button is provided which will light up all of the segments displaying an eight. The user can then easily determine if one or more of the segments are malfunctioning.

Displayed Symbol	Binary Value
⌐│ └┘	0000
│ │	0001

117

	0010
	0011
	0100
	0101
	0110
	0111
	1000
	1001
	1010
	1011
	1100
	1101
	1110
	1111

Figure 1:   Seven Segment Display Output

A simple data representation of two positions may be obtained from a single output port as shown below.

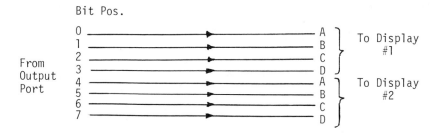

Figure 2: Simple Interface

This configuration will display the data in BCD or hexadecimal format, provided the data is appropriately coded and the correct decoder/driver is used.

Octal representation of an output port may be obtained using either a BCD or hex decoder/driver and connecting it according to the following chart.

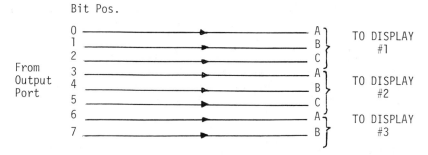

Figure 3: Octal Display Representation

Of course, additional digits of accuracy may be obtained by using additional output ports and the methods described above. However, a

119

bit more additional hardware or software can result in up to 16 digits
of display on a single port.

The technique simply requires the use of an additional 4 line to
16 line decoder such as a 74154 IC. The first bits of the output port
may be used to enable a particular display and the second 4 bits of the
port may dictate the digit to be displayed. It is assumed that in this
configuration each display unit contains its own decoder/driver.

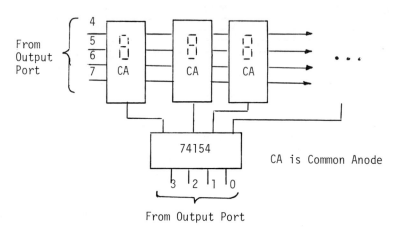

From Output Port

Figure 4: Display Multiplexing

The operation of this circuit is as follows. The value of the digit
to be outputted is presented on the lines, 4, 5, 6, 7 of the I/O port.
Simultaneously, the position of the digit is outputted on lines 0, 1,
2, 3. The given digit will light. The processor can be programmed to
hold that digit for a prescribed period of time before proceeding to
the next digit. If the time delay is reasonable (to be experimentally
derived), the digits may be scanned in turn to produce the effect of
a continuously lighted display. Up to 16 BCD or hex positions may be
displayed using a single 8 bit I/O port.

Still another technique may be used in lieu of the constant scanning method by providing a latch on each display. Some decoder/drivers
already have this feature built in, such as the 9370 IC. This particular configuration requires that the data to be displayed be presented
to the seven segment display and then, a short time later, a latching
pulse be applied to the clock input of the latch. The short time delay may be accomplished using a one-shot multivibrator such as a 74121
IC.

Prelaboratory Investigation

1. Using a seven segment display, it is possible to construct a
   representation of all but a few letters of the alphabet using a
   combination of upper and lower case displays. List all of the
   valid letters.

2. Write a program which will, from an external clock, count the pulses and display their value from 0-9999 using the circuit shown in figure 4. The time each display is on and the speed at which the display is refreshed should be adjustable.

3. Design a latching type four digit display configuration as discussed in the background investigation which uses a minimum of standard integrated circuits.

4. Modify the program in step 2 above so that it may be used with latching type display modules. (Note: This should require deleting certain statements only.)

Laboratory Investigation

1. Construct the circuit shown in figure 4.

2. Using the processor to count the pulses from the external generator, using the program from step 2 of the prelaboratory investigation, adjust the "on" time and "refresh" time for the displays so that the displays can be read consistently.

3. Determine the minimum time required such that the displays will not "flicker".

4. Construct a latching type display configuration as described in the latter portion of the background investigation.

5. Using the circuit and program from steps 3 and 4 of the prelaboratory analysis, verify the correct operation of the display.

Questions for Further Study

1. List the advantages and disadvantages for both the latching and nonlatching type multiplexed data displays.

2. Survey the market and determine the cost and availability of multiplexed data displays. What are the signals required for operation?

3. Using two eight bit data I/O ports, how many displays may be used for output? Describe the connections that may be used.

Experiment 20

HARDWARE DIAGNOSTIC TECHNIQUES

Purpose

An introduction into diagnostics of the hardware aspects of the microprocessor system will be discussed in this experiment.

Background Investigation

The most refined portion of any microprocessor based system is the hardware. The software is more apt to change from application to application and can possibly be totally different if the same application were made by two different designers; however, the hardware will most likely be the same. Totally designed hardware systems including RAM, ROM (PROM), digital I/O, and serial interfaces are available to suit a variety of applications. These products can be purchased that have undergone a "burn-in" period and have extended the MTBF (mean time between failure) to almost infinity. In addition, the cost of the hardware components has decreased to such a level that, when something does go wrong, the whole unit may be discarded.

Some applications still require a high reliability factor. Microcomputers are becoming the center of systems that cannot tolerate a hardware failure. Medical instrumentation, aircraft systems and even some automotive applications require redundancies built in to prevent a catastrophic situation from developing. In systems such as these, a self-diagnostic routine may insure that massive failures do not exist. Even in systems used in the home entertainment area, service technicians may not have the required training to troubleshoot problems down to the IC level. If the microprocessor can conduct its own troubleshooting from the hardware level, much time and hair pulling can be saved.

The self diagnosis of the hardware condition can be divided into two major areas, memory and interface. The microprocessor itself is assumed to be functional for the tests conducted. If the diagnostic routines fail to run correctly, it can only be due to the processor itself or the associated PROM, ROM devices.

Quick, cursory system checks may be devised based on the hardware and processor used. These must be developed with an intimate knowledge of the particular configuration. For example, if an INTEL 8080 or 8085 system is in use with RAM beginning at memory address 0, then the short program

                        DCR SP

                        RST 0

may be entered at location 0. This program will clear all RAM memory locations. First, the stack pointer is decremented by one. Next, the system will do a restart 0, push the contents of the PC onto the stack (PC at this point is [000 001_8]) and begin execution at location 0. The 000_8 portion of the PC is push first followed by 001_8. When the SP is decremented by 1, the 001_8 is lost leaving only the 000 on the stack. Eventually, the entire memory will be cleared. This provides a quick and easy check to determine if the basic components of the system are functional.

    Less machine dependent procedures may be developed for checking the RAM portion of the system. A program could be developed to:

    1. Write all ones into each memory location,

    2. Read the locations noting any exceptions,

    3. Write all zeros into each memory location,

    4. Read and note exceptions,

    5. Write an alternating 1-0 bit pattern into memory,

    6. Read and note exceptions.

Other memory check programs exist but essentially operate the same way.

    PROM programmers have a self-checking routine integral with the system that allows the user to compare one PROM against another. In dedicated system applications that extensively use PROM, a hardware interface may be devised to allow this comparison to be made as part of the normal diagnostic procedure. One PROM socket could be provided. Programmatically select an internal PROM and compare it against a standard. A less rigorous procedure may be employed by using a checksum routine. The single precision sum (MOD 2) of all the PROM or ROM memory locations can be made, discarding the carry bit. The result can then be compared to the known checksum for the PROM. If it matches, chances (256:1) are that the PROM is correct and has not been altered. Other checksum operations such as AND, OR, EX-OR, etc., may also be employed.

    To test the I/O interface, a simple procedure involves connecting LEDs to all digital output lines, and slide switches to all digital input lines. A simple routine to input the switch settings and immediately output the values to the LEDs will allow the operator to test for an I/O failure. Each bit may be tested independently. If the I/O port in use uses a connector for the interface, such as a standard DB-25, a special cable may be constructed that connects each input bit directly to the corresponding output bit. A resident program in PROM may be developed to test the interface independent of operator intervention.

Often, where the operation of the I/O interface is critical, two interface devices may be used. The second device would "read" the output of the first device to insure the correct value has been transmitted. If the system employs A/D and D/A converters scaled for the same voltage swing, a similar procedure may be followed.

Very often students are positive that the microprocessor does not execute a particular instruction correctly. The likelihood of this happening is very minimal. Odds are that the program was not correctly written or the flag bits were not properly set. To help to illustrate the fact that the instructions are properly functioning, several instruction test routines can be developed.

1. Jump test

2. Data transfer test

3. Arithmetic instruction test

4. Logical instruction test

Combined with a previously stored table of test values, the processor can be programmed to test each instruction to insure the correct performance.

Prelaboratory Investigation

1. Select an "indication device" that will show proper operation or failure based on the diagnostic procedures to be developed.

2. Develop a memory check procedure to test the memory of the microcomputer used to run the experiments.

3. Develop an I/O interface test procedure to insure the proper operation of serial, parallel and analog ports as available on your microcomputer.

4. Select a particular group of instructions as outlined in the background investigation and develop a test program.

5. Program the procedures from steps 2 through 4 above. The program should include a checksum test at the beginning to insure that it properly operates.

Laboratory Investigation

1. Program the test procedures on PROM for permanent installation on your system. Note: this procedure may be used to check the system performance before each experiment.

2. Test the system using the developed procedure.

3. Purposely install faulty integrated circuits to test the capability of the system.

4. How long does it take to do a complete system test?

Questions for Further Study

1. What other error checking codes are popular? Which test serial data? Which test parallel data?

2. List other self-diagnostic hardware procedures that may be included on your system.

3. How often should the self-diagnostic tests be performed?

4. When is an integrated circuit most likely to fail?

Experiment 21

7490 DECADE COUNTER TEST FIXTURE

Purpose

In this experiment, the use of the microcomputer to test integrated circuits will be studied. Specifically, a method to conduct a partial test of the TTL 7490 will be discussed.

Background Investigation

Automated testing has become increasingly important in recent years. Many of the integrated circuits used in consumer and industrial products perform numerous functions and it is difficult to conduct a complete test without resorting to some form of automation. Even though the reliability of integrated circuits far surpasses their discrete counterparts, the complexity of these devices increases the probability that something can go wrong. The highest probability of failure for the integrated circuit is during the first 100 hours of operation. This is the reason that many manufacturers subject the devices to an initial burn-in period. After that time, the devices must be retested.

Manufacturers of integrated circuit systems often spend more time in testing than they do in manufacturing. As much as 70% of the time from incoming inspection of components to outgoing finished products may be spent in testing. Because the microprocessor is intended for control and the fact that it is easily programmed, makes it an ideal choice for the automated testing of circuits, components and devices.

The testing of most products begins with an incoming inspection. Devices, such as individual integrated circuits, may be tested for functional specifications as well as cosmetic defects. SSI, MSI and particularly LSI circuits must be quickly and efficiently tested. In this experiment, a procedure for testing one particular integrated circuit will be presented. Only a portion of the 7490's functional capability will be tested due to the extent of development time required to form a complete testing procedure. Similar procedures may be developed to test any IC. A generalized program which calls upon specifics from a data table could be developed to test an entire IC family, even though pin connections and power requirements vary. Analog switches and transmission gates can be used to provide a means for the microcomputer to "wire" each IC to be tested. These IC testers are presently being sold throughout the country.

The BCD counting capabilities and the reset modes of the 7490 are to be tested. The external pin connections will be made to an I/O port and the power supplies will be made according to the diagram shown in figure 1.

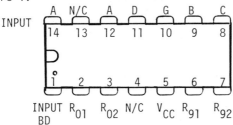

Figure 1: Pin-Outs for the 7490

Table 1 below shows the Reset/Count inputs necessary to either reset the device to all zero outputs, preset the outputs to 9 for a countdown or enable the device to count in normal BCD. The inputs to the chip, R_{01}, R_{02}, R_{91}, R_{92} will be set based on an I/O port configuration.

Condition	R_{01}	R_{02}	R_{91}	R_{92}	D	C	B	A
1	1	1	X	X	0	0	0	0
2	X	X	1	1	1	0	0	1
3	0	0	0	0	C	O	U	N T

X signifies a don't care term.

Table 1: Reset, Preset and Count Modes

For operation as a BCD counter, the BD input must be externally connected to the A output. In this case, the pulse signal for BCD counting must be externally connected to the INPUT A terminal. The resulting BCD counting sequence appears in Table 2.

BCD COUNT SEQUENCE

Table 2:

COUNT	OUTPUT			
	D	C	B	A
0	0	0	0	0
1	0	0	0	1
2	0	0	1	0
3	0	0	1	1
.				
.				
9	1	0	0	1

127

Figure 2 shows the I/O connections. Input to the microprocessor will be the 7490 outputs ABCD. The outputs from the microprocessor will include a clock pulse (Bit 0), a bad chip and a good chip indicator (Bits 1 and 2), and the reset/count outputs (Bits 4, 5, 6 and 7).

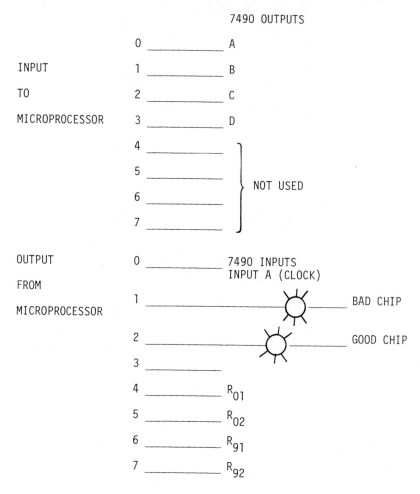

Figure 2: I/O Port Connections

A complete flowchart for the test procedure appears in figure 3. Initially the program checks the reset and preset conditions to insure their proper function and then proceeds to test the BCD counting sequence.

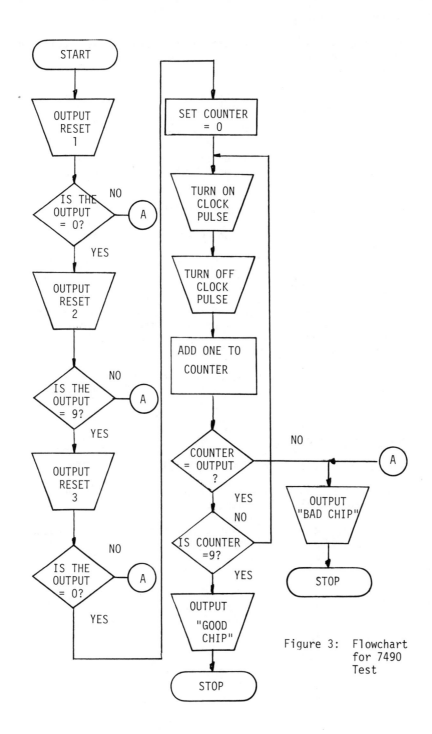

Figure 3: Flowchart for 7490 Test

Prelaboratory Investigation

1. Using the manufacturer's specifications for the 7490, determine the characteristics of the clock pulse. Does it trigger on a rising or falling edge?

2. Draw a more specific flowchart for the program depected in figure 3. Use specific register names and specify their content.

3. Code the flowchart into machine or assembly language.

4. A problem may develop when the reset condition 3 is outputted. The count (0-9) may advance before the first clock pulse is generated.

   a) Determine the cause of this problem,

   b) Why is a possible solution to add a 10 μsec delay before the reset is outputted?

Laboratory Investigation

1. Verify the correct operation of the interface circuit by writing a simple program to input and output to the ports in use. (This is done to insure problems that may arise are due to programming problems and not hardware.)

2. When the program is operational and the problems with reset condition 3 have been resolved, test several 7490s that will be supplied in class.

Questions for Further Study

1. What would have to be done to completely test the 7490 IC?

2. Design a test unit that will functionally check the operation of any combinational 7400 series IC.

3. List the parameters for an integrated circuit that may not be easily tested using a microprocessor based tester.

Experiment 22

INTERRUPT CHARACTERISTICS

Purpose

The purpose of this experiment is to investigate the various aspects of program interrupts from both the hardware and software considerations.

Background Investigation

Applications involving microprocessor systems seem to perform a variety of tasks simultaneously. Even large computer systems operating in a time shared mode perform tasks for multiple users while appearing to give their sole attention to an individual user. This ability to create an illusion of being able to do more than one task at a time is due to the speed of the computer system and interrupts.

Microprocessor applications that demand much of the available computing time use interrupts almost exclusively to categorize and queue the various tasks to be performed. Peripheral devices are most often tied to the interrupt facility because they are the slowest devices in the system. It is not a wise use of computer time to sit and constantly poll an input device waiting for data or to wait for a mechanical printer to type a character. Systems such as this are said to be I/O bound. In other words, the upper bound to through-put is dependent on the speed of the I/O device. It is much more efficient to have a system divide its time efficiently between computation and I/O to do the maximum amount of work in the shortest period of time.

Consider, for example, the case where a keyboard is used as an input device. Two methods may be used to retrieve the input data. One is based on the processor polling or waiting for an entry from the user. This procedure requires a disproportionately high percentage of the computer's time. In cases such as this, the processor would wait in a loop and perform the following:

1. Input the keyboard status information,

2. Check the status bit to determine if a key has been depressed.

Typically, the above sequence of operations may only require 10 microseconds to execute, even considering a slow processor.

131

A reasonable typing speed would require a three second wait in between characters. Thus:

$$\frac{3 \text{ seconds}}{10 \text{ microseconds/loop}} = 300,000$$

It can be seen that the processor would execute this loop a total of 300,000 times for each character. Instructions in excess of 600,000 could be executed in the same time period thus enhancing the available computing capabilities.

Types of devices that may be connected to an interrupt input of the processor include keyboards, printers, various input signals and even fail-safe devices. A fail-safe device may demand the immediate attention of the processor regardless of its present task. Even some programs may have a higher priority than others and a software interrupt may be generated.

In a system that is totally dependent on hardware and software interrupts the processor must be doing something. The program it is executing in this task oriented system is called a background program. It may be nothing more than a program which counts continually. When a device or program requests service, the system will exit the background program, service the interrupt and return.

Interrupt service routines on most systems act much like a subroutine call statement. When the processor receives an interrupt request, it finishes the instruction it is currently executing and then immediately branches to the service routine which is stored at a predetermined address. Upon completion of the task procedure, program control is passed back to the background program. Some systems do not require a background program because they may be interrupted from a halt.

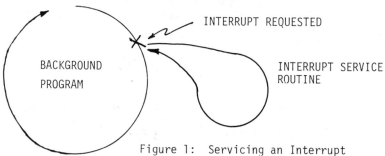

Figure 1: Servicing an Interrupt

The starting address for an interrupt service routine may be determined two ways:

1. The processor always branches to a routine stored at the same address,

2. The address of the service routine is stored at a

particular memory location.

The method used depends on the particular processor being employed.

Two types of interrupts may be employed in microprocessor systems. Maskable interrupts are of the type that may be turned on and off or ignored when the occasion arises. The non-maskable interrupts are always activated and may never be disabled. This type of interrupt would be most often employed to service fail-safe interrupts. Both are available on some systems while the maskable variety only may be found on others.

In summary, the following steps outline the interrupt process:

1. The processor may be executing a series of instructions called a background program,

2. In the case of maskable interrupts, the interrupts must be turned on or enabled,

3. An interrupt request is sent to the processor via a signal to a particular pin or through a program via a software interrupt,

4. When an interrupt request is received, the processor will complete the instruction it is currently executing and disable the interrupt system (maskable),

5. The processor then branches to, or obtains the address of the interrupt service routine and saves the return address on the stack,

6. At this point, depending on the service routine and the processor used, the contents of the internal registers may be saved on the stack,

7. The interrupt is then serviced,

8. Before returning to the background program, the contents of the internal registers should be restored and, in the case of maskable interrupts, the interrupts should be enabled,

9. A subroutine return or a return from interrupt instruction is then executed allowing program control to be returned to the background program.

Hardware connections to the interrupt inputs of the processor vary widely, the simplest of which may be nothing more than a direct connection to the INT or $\overline{INT}$ line of the chip. When an interrupt signal is generated, the processor triggers on the using edge of the signal. Further interrupts will not be acknowledged until another rising edge signal is received (provided the interrupts are enabled in the maskable case).

Other microprocessors require the interrupt line to remain active until the signal is acknowledged by the processor. In cases such as this, an INTA or interrupt acknowledge signal is provided. External hardware may be required to: 1) set a flip-flop when the interrupt is requested, 2) clear the flip-flop when the interrupt is acknowledged.

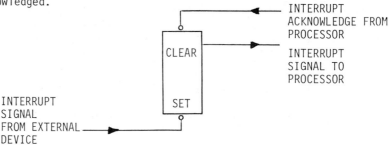

Figure 2:   Interrupt Hardware

In still other processors such as the Intel 8080, an instruction called a restart (RST) instruction must be "jammed" on to the data bus during the INTA active signal. During this time the other devices such as memory and I/O, also connected to the bus, must be tri-stated.

Understanding the interrupt function and its subtle characteristics will make this feature invaluable in a variety of applications.

Prelaboratory Investigation

1. Determine the answers to the following questions regarding the particular microprocessor in use.

    a) Does the microprocessor have more than one interrupt input?

    b) Which of the interrupt inputs are maskable or non-maskable?

    c) How is the interrupt service routine's address determined?

    d) What is the maximum and minimum length of the interrupt request signal?

    e) Are further interrupts automatically disabled after the initial request?

    f) What information about the background program is automatically saved when program control is transferred to the interrupt routine?

    g) Will the processor "remember" an interrupt if a signal is generated while the interrupts are disabled?

    h) Once the interrupt routine has been properly executed, what instruction is required to return to the background program?

2. Draw a flowchart for a procedure which will rotate a single bit through the accumulator and carry position and an interrupt routine that will simply count the number of times the processor has been interrupted and store this value in a predetermined memory location.

3. Write the routines for the flowchart in Step 2 above.

Laboratory Investigation

1. Determine the procedure for accessing the interrupt line of the microprocessor from a hardware standpoint:

   a) Does the interrupt line require a positive or negative logic signal?

   b) What pulse duration is required?

   c) Does the processor acknowledge the receipt of the interrupt?

   d) Is the interrupt line edge triggered? If so, what is the effect of a constant voltage applied to the input?

2. Connect a debounced pulser to the interrupt line as called for by the microprocessor in use.

3. Verify the correct operation of the program written in Step 3 of the prelaboratory investigation by counting interrupt signals.

Questions for Further Investigation

1. If a particular application requires several devices to be connected to the interrupt line, how may the processor distinguish between them?

2. Why are interrupts used?

3. List at least ten specific devices which could be connected to the interrupt facility.

4. What are the differences between an interrupt and direct memory access (DMA)?

5. What are the possible ramifications of an interrupt interpreting an interrupt?

Experiment 23

VECTORED AND PRIORITY INTERRUPTS

Purpose

The purpose of this experiment is to investigate the advantages of employing vectored and priority interrupt facilities in microprocessor systems.

Background Investigation

Interrupts are similar to a call subroutine instruction, but have the added feature that they may be placed anywhere in a program based on the action of external hardware. Interrupts are used on most systems for a peripheral device to gain attention of the microprocessor. A fail-safe device in a particular application may demand the immediate attention of the processor, for example, or a keyboard or other device may also request a response from the system.

When accepted, the interrupt results in a branch to a service routine which preserves its internal registers, if required, and performs the appropriate function. Program execution resumes upon completion of the service routine.

Several devices may be connected to the interrupt line of the microprocessor. Each interrupting device may require its own handler or service routine that may be located at different addresses. A scheme whereby program control for each interrupting device is automatically transferred to the appropriate memory address is called vectoring. Some microprocessors have built-in vectored interrupts such as the 8080. The 8080 eight interrupt vectors may be employed. Additional vectors may be added with additional software and/or hardware. For the purposes of this experiment, vectoring will be done with a combination of external hardware and software and the microprocessor will be assumed to have only a single level interrupt capability.

In addition to the capability of vectoring an interrupt to a particular address, a priority may be assigned to the interrupting device. Due to the wide variety of applications for the interrupt, various devices may be more important and require a priority. For example, a fail-safe device would naturally have a higher priority than, say, a Teletype or keyboard I/O device. Priority is, therefore, an order assigned to an event or device which determines the order in which it will be serviced. Usually a number is assigned to each device with "0" being the highest priority, (sometimes assigned to power-fail detection circuitry).

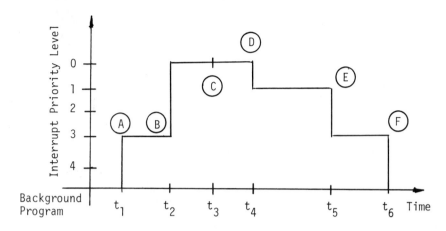

Figure 1: Typical Interrupt Sequence

A simple graph, shown in figure 1, may be used to illustrate the procedure that is followed when servicing interrupts with differing priority levels. The processor is executing a background program when no interrupts are requesting action. A sequence of events for the interrupts and the required servicing is given below.

Point	Event
A	Device with priority level 3 requests an interrupt. Processor exits background program and begins interrupt servicing (t_1)
B	Device 0 requests an interrupt and it is serviced because it has a higher level priority (t_2)
C	Device 1 requests an interrupt but must wait until device 0 has been serviced (t_3)
D	Service of device 0 completed. Begins interrupt level 1 servicing (t_4)
E	Service of device 1 completed. Returns to level 3 to complete service routine (t_5)
F	Servicing of device 3 completed. Returns to background program since no other devices are requesting an interrupt.

A hardware scheme may be devised to handle the interrupting and priority coding for this system. A simplified version of this is shown in figure 2.

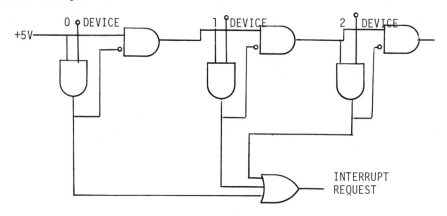

Figure 2: A Priority Interrupt Scheme

In the diagram above, note that if the highest priority level 0 requests an interrupt, lower level devices are "locked out" and will not be serviced until the higher level device has been serviced. This same procedure may be accomplished using software but requires addition- al processor time to complete the action.

Due to the fact that interrupt request lines are typically edge triggered, if an interrupt is generated at a lower level, the signal must be "remembered". When the higher level interrupts have been serviced, a new pulse should be generated. This may be accomplished by using a flop-flop device on each line to retain the information until the processor can, in turn, recognize each interrupt signal.

Still another method of accomplishing the same end is based on a method which employs software to vector or prioritize the interrupt signals. A simple hardware connection as shown in figure 3 is used to signal the processor whenever an interrupt request is received from any of the four different devices. (Note: It is assumed that the highest priority device is device 0.) When the interrupt is activated, a routine will determine the following:

1) Is a higher priority device currently being serviced? (This may be accomplished by reserving a status word in memory that may be interrogated by any routine to determine the action being taken.)

2) Which device is requesting the service and at what location is the service routine stored?

3) Have all devices that have previously requested service, that are of a higher priority, been serviced?

4) The interrupts should be re-enabled at this point so that subsequent interrupts may be acknowledged.

After each interrupt routine is completed, the status word in memory should be checked to determine if a lower priority device is still requesting service before control is finally passed back to the background program.

DEVICE #

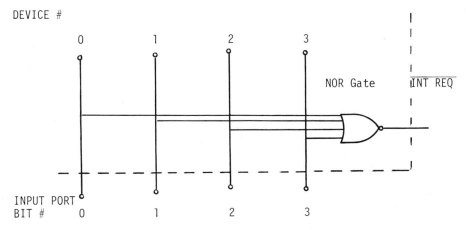

Figure 3: External Hardware Connections

Prelaboratory Investigation

1. Determine the following regarding the characteristics of the microprocessor system being used:

   a) Are vectored interrupts available as a standard feature?

   b) If vectored interrupts are available, how many levels?

   c) Does the system include all available hardware to make them usable?

   d) Are priority levels available as a standard hardware feature?

2. Draw a flowchart to implement the vectored and priority interrupt scheme discussed. Four levels of interrupts should be used. Each service routine should output, to a seven segment display, the device code (0,1,2 or 3) for a period of two seconds and then return to the background program. The background program should constantly output an 8 to the display.

3. Code, into machine langauge, the flowchart written in step 2.

4. Draw a complete hardware priority system using only commonly available TTL components.

Laboratory Investigation

1. Test the vectored and priority program from step 3 of the prelaboratory analysis by interrupting the background program at all possible levels and noting the displayed results.

2. Attempt to interrupt the program above from higher priority levels and note the result.

3. Verify the correct operation of the TTL priority scheme developed in step 4 of the prelaboratory analysis.

Questions for Further Study

1. If a system contains many I/O devices that are frequently used, which of the devices should have the highest priority, the fastest or slowest device?

2. Categorize each of the following microprocessors as to interrupt vectoring and priority availability:

   a) 8080

   b) 8048

   c) 8085

   d) 8086

   e) 6800

   f) 6809

   g) 68000

   h) Z80

3) Classify each of the following devices with a priority level (0 to 6, 0 is the highest):

   a) disk drive   e) alarm switch

   b) 30 cps printer   f) keyboard

   c) 300 lpm printer   g) display test push button

   d) power failure detector

Experiment 24

AN INTERRUPT DRIVEN REAL TIME CLOCK

Purpose

The purpose of this experiment is to investigate the use of interrupts to produce an accurate, real time clock.

Background Investigation

A timing loop is often used in microprocessor programs to provide an appropriate delay action or to provide a wait state for further action. The timing loop has a particular drawback in that, while the computer is counting out the delay, no other action or computations can take place. In fact, in a program where an output device or devices must be polled on a regular basis, the job of calculating precise time delay becomes rather involved. A real time clock, driven by an interrupt, becomes a reasonable alternative. The processor is connected via the interrupt line to the 60 Hz line. Sixty times per second, the processor updates the clock counting locations in memory. Because it is connected to the interrupt line, the operation becomes almost transparent to the other system operations. Whenever the precise time is required, a program can simply interrogate the hours, minutes and seconds storage locations in memory. Timing formats are software dependent and thus easily modified to suit a particular application.

The time may be stored in BCD format by counting the pulse train based on the 60 Hz AC line. The resulting time may be either stored or outputted to seven segment displays. A typical configuration for the 60 Hz line adapter appears in figure 1.

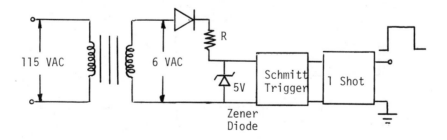

Figure 1: 60 Hz Adapter

The transformer provides isolation and reduces the output voltage to an appropriate voltage level. The Schmitt trigger circuit provides the wave shaping and the one-shot multivibrator provides an adjustment of the pulse width output. In many dedicated microprocessor systems, it is not necessary to employ the one-shot multivibrator to limit the "ON" time. A feedback signal from the microprocessor is provided to reset the interrupt facility. This signal may be available from the status information and is the interrupt acknowledge.

A flowchart of the interrupt service routine appears in figure 2 to produce a twelve hour display of hours, minutes, and seconds.

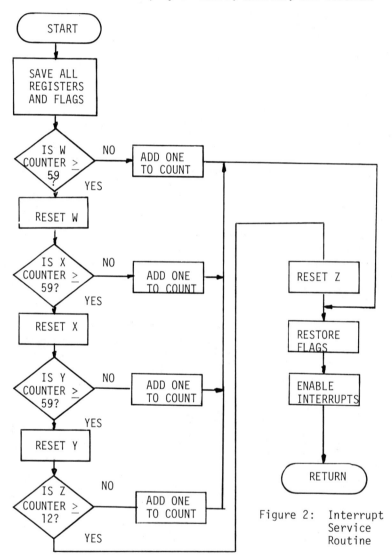

Figure 2: Interrupt Service Routine

Prelaboratory Investigation

1. Write the interrupt service routine as called for in the flowchart of figure 2.

2. Develop a simple background program to be used in conjunction with this routine which will constantly output the hours, minutes and seconds derived from the interrupt routine.

3. Draw a complete schematic diagram that may be used in the construction of the 60 Hz adapter shown in figure 1. (Note: An opto-isolator may be employed to reduce the possibility of damage to the computer's interrupt line.)

Laboratory Investigation

1. Test the programs written in steps 1 and 2 of the prelaboratory investigation using an external 0-5 volt variable rate clock pulse.

2. Note the effect of varying the clock speed and pulse width on the system timing and record the observations made.

3. Independently test the 60 Hz adapter to insure the correct pulse width and desired precision.

4. Verify the correct operation of the total system.

Questions for Further Study

1. Using estimates of the length of time for execution of the interrupt service routine and the 60 Hz line frequency, calculate a total estimate of the percent of available processor time spent updating the clock's information.

2. If the microprocessor system uses a video terminal, modify the programs in this experiment to constantly output the hours, minutes and seconds display in the upper right corner of the screen in the format:

   XX:XX:XX

3. Develop a list of microprocessor based consumer products available on the market which use or could use this real time clock program.

Experiment 25

THE DESIGN PROCESS

Purpose

This experiment will summarize the aspects of microprocessor system design by outlining the steps in the design process. A practical example of the application of these principles will be developed.

Background Investigation

Many of the topics treated in the courses in electrical programs can apply directly to the design of a microprocessor based system. Courses such as writing and composition pertain to the documentation. Courses in electronics and circuit analysis apply to the interface design. Even courses in high level programming languages increase one's algorithmic development skills and provide a broad background from which to write more sophisticated machine language programs. The ideal design process brings together talents and skills in an organized manner for the proper solution to the application problem.

Some microprocessor based consumer products on the market used the device for namesake only. "Computer Controlled", "The only one available with a brain", "Intelligent" are phrases often used. These devices may use less than one percent of the processing time available and virtually none of the sophistication. Some products use the microprocessor only as a clock. It seems that with only slightly more software and virtually no additional hardware, these products could utilize the full power and timesaving features of the microprocessor system. Software and documentation seem to be the two areas that require the most forethought and planning. Hardware devices have far surpassed the state-of-the-art in these other two areas. Cost is also a factor in the software and documentation area. Mass-produced hardware can be used in most applications, but software must be tailor-made to suite each application.

Certain steps can be summarized in the design of any device, process or system. These are given on the following pages, only modified slightly to pertain to microprocessors. Although design engineers do not carry a card around with them when they go about this process, everyone at one time or another has become familiar with these principles.

1. Problem Definition. The initial step is probably the most important and the most often overlooked. A trend begins with the first step and it is fundamental to begin the process on the right foot with a thorough investigation into the characteristics of the problem. Try to live with the problem for a few days and document its important components.

   Many individuals are quick to offer possible solutions at this point. This must be avoided. When the boss calls you in to make a design assignment, he may tell you more of his ideas for the solution than the components of the problem. Find out everything you can about the problem by consulting any available source. Be sure to determine all potential trouble areas.

2. Develop Possible Solutions. This will occur before a flowchart is even drawn. A list of specific requirements should be developed from the problem definition. Avoid phrases such as "will have lower power consumption" and replace them with "will use less than 10 watts". A matrix can then be developed of possible ideas vs. the problem requirements. Obviously the best solution would be the one that satisfies the most user requirements. This process becomes a modified brainstorming session.

3. Interface Hardware. Before the actual development of the algorithms can be made, the system interface hardware must be thought out. Some of the duties may be delegated to external logic circuits depending on how heavily the microprocessor is being utilized. Decisions made at this point regarding the hardware-software trade-off problem are intended to be preliminary and may be modified at a later time.

4. Draw the Flowchart. Many designers feel that this step is a waste of time and prefer to sit at a terminal and compose the program. In large projects, where many people are involved, the flowchart becomes the common basis for interchange of ideas. In addition, a flowchart may keep the programmer from getting lost and "not being able to see the forest for the trees". In the development of the flowchart for the program, it may be wise to draw two. The first should be very general in nature and not detail out the requirements of individual routines. Terms common to the problem area, standard mathematical phraseology and English should be used exclusively. A second flowchart may be drawn for the entire process or individual routines in a more detailed fashion for the individual processor being used. Again, however, placing instructions in the boxes should be avoided. This conveys little additional information that could not be found in the program listing. Using English relieves the programmer of the burden of remembering all of the instructions and their format.

5. Write the Program. The programming process can be somewhat simplified if a good flowchart can be used as a guide. Two approaches to the coding are better than one. Problems in the flowchart are

often uncovered when the program is written and bugs in the program are avoided by a well thought-out flowchart. If the programming system allows for comment statements, they should be included. It is not necessary to identify each statement, but only major routines or justifications for approaches so that they may be easily identified during the debugging process. Modularize the program whenever possible using subroutines that may be tested independently.

6. Revise and Evaluate. After the program has been written, it may be necessary to revise the flowchart. It should be kept as current as possible. In addition, the interface hardware may be in need of revision, modification or updating.

7. Construct the Interface Hardware. Test and evaluate the interface hardware to insure its proper operation and appropriateness for the application.

8. Prototype the Entire System. Using an organized and piecewise approach, test each phase of the hardware and software before attempting to run the entire system. Do not become over anxious to see the entire system operate. This may often lead to more and more delays.

9. Design the Dedicated Hardware. If the system is to be a totally stand alone or turn-key, it is now time to design the hardware keeping in mind cost, space requirements, power consumption, etc. The interface circuitry used in the prototyping phase should be easily modified to fit the dedicated equipment.

10. Modify Software. Because much of the software may appear on PROM or ROM it may be necessary to modify it to be relocatable or utilize less RAM area than previously used. In addition modifications of the dedicated hardware over the prototype system may necessitate other changes.

11. Implement the Total Design. In a piecewise approach, again, test the total design. Does it solve the problem as originally intended? Does it meet the problem requirements? At this point it may be a good idea to stand back and look at the system as a whole or from the user's point of view.

12. Documentation. Finally, after months of work, the system is designed and ready for production. However, one of the steps in the process that may influence people to purchase it or evaluate your design is still left to be done, the documentation. This step should not be left to a third party, possibly not properly familiar with all of the features. It should be done by the person who completes the design. View the documentation from the user's end. Documentation can be tested and should. Choose other individuals who are not familiar with your work, and, using only the supplied documentation, have them figure out how it works or how to use it.

In case it has gone unnoticed, the steps involved in this design process comprise an algorithm. Although it is not necessary to follow each step in every design, they may be used as a guide and should be referred to frequently. Many long and frustrating hours can be saved in the solution of a problem if only it is approached in a logical manner.

Prelaboratory Investigation

It is desired to design a replacement for the mechanical time clocks used in factory environments. The device should have the following characteristics:

1. microprocessor based,

2. expandable from one unit to many,

3. able to communicate with a central computer, if available,

4. cost less, in quantity production, than presently available mechanical clocks,

5. other requirements as appropriate (see problem definition step 1).

For the above system complete steps 1 through 4 of the design process as described in the background investigation.

Laboratory Investigation

Using a group approach, critique the initial design steps by discussing the appropriateness of each routine, circuit or problem requirement.

Questions for Further Study

Select a microprocessor based product currently on the market and evaluate it in comparison to the 12 design steps that were presented in this experiment. Did the designer properly approach the problem as evidenced by a meaningful design?

D/A CONVERSION PRINCIPLES

Purpose

The principles of digital to analog converters and operating characteristics of several D/A converter circuits will be discussed in this experiment.

Background Investigation

Analog signals are of prime importance when investigating any microcomputer application where it is desirable to interface to the outside world. Most signals available from real world devices are of the analog variety. Furthermore, most transducers produce an analog output proportional to the input and control of these devices is usually derived from an analog signal. Microprocessors have been used in a variety of applications such as radios, automobiles, TV games and process control. These applications would not be possible without a method of converting the analog signals to and from the digital format necessary for the microcomputer. A/D and D/A must be well understood by the potential system designer and because many of the A/D principles are based on an understanding of D/A converters, D/A will be covered first.

The D/A converter may be used in systems to control output devices as previously discussed, but in addition, the analog output is desirable to produce pseudo triangular and sinusoidal waveforms needed for machine control; meters for output voltage, frequency and current measurements; stripchart recorder outputs; servomotor drive circuits; and voltage controlled oscillators. Some devices may require a complex waveform which may be derived from a table stored in the microcomputer's memory.

The D/A converter does not produce a true continuously variable analog output voltage, but rather a piecewise approximation. Take, for example, the waveforms shown in figure 1. The desired waveform shown in figure 1 (a) can be approximately reproduced by the computer as shown in figure 1 (b).

Figure 1:
Analog Output
Reproduction

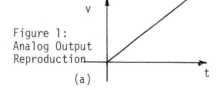

(a)

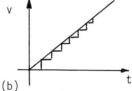

(b)

The maximum voltage output as well as the rate at which the D/A converter can follow the waveform is dictated by two important factors, i.e., the number of bits of precision of the converter and the speed of the processor and associated software. These factors work together to produce the desired output.

Important specifications are included in most manufacturers' literature regarding digital to analog converters (DACs). These include, but are not limited to, accuracy, resolution, linearity, settling time, slew rate, overshoot and conversion rate. Several DACs will be discussed in the following paragraphs. Each one may be interfaced to the microcomputer unit to produce a piecewise approximation to an analog waveform.

The first method of D/A conversion is probably the simplest, requiring the least software to support. Its operation is based on a device called a transmission gate. The device is similar in operation to a tri-state buffer. The CD4016 quad bilateral switch is an example of this type of gate. Its logic symbol is shown in figure 2 along with a simpler model that may be used.

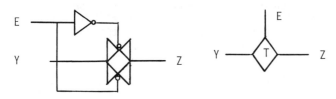

Figure 2: Bidirectional Analog Switch

When a logical one signal is applied to the E (enable) input, a low impedance path between Z and Y is established. In this condition, the device is considered on and will allow a signal to pass in either direction. When a logical zero is applied to E, the path Z to Y is a high impedance condition and the device is considered to be off. More devices of this type exist, such as the eight channel analog multiplexer, which may be used in similar applications. The voltage applied to E is typically the logical 0-5 volts, while the inputs/outputs Y and Z work in the range of ±15 volts. Using the voltage divider principle, a very simple D/A converter may be constructed as shown in figure 3.

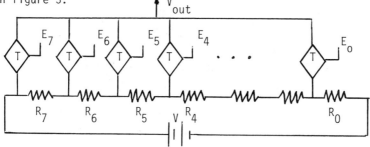

Figure 3: Simple Digital To Analog Converter

The enable inputs to the transmission gates may be connected to the I/O port of the microcomputer. When each gate is activated singularly, the output voltage produced is proportional to the voltage divider and may be determined using the following formula:

$$V_{out} = \frac{R_x}{\sum_{i=1}^{7} R_i}$$

If $R_0 = R_1 = R_2 \ldots = R_7$, then the output voltage is divided into 8 equal values. When gate V_0 is activated, then $V_0 = V/8$. Similarly, when E_6 is active, then $V_0 = 7V/8$ and when E_7 is active, then $V_0 = V$. The staircase waveform may be generated by initializing the accumulator to one and simply rotating the bit through the accumulator. When the bit being rotated is in the carry position, all gates will be disabled and the resulting V_0 will be approximately zero.

This configuration has some disadvantages in that only 8 different levels of output voltage may be achieved. This will severely limit the resolution which can be obtained. Only one gate may be activated at a time; multiple enable signals will effectively short out the resistors in the circuit, increasing the current drain from the source.

The second method to be discussed involves the use of the operational amplifier summing network shown in figure 4. This circuit is familiar to those who have studied feedback amplifiers. The output voltage e_0 may be shown to be

$$e_0 = -e_1 \frac{R_f}{R_1} - e_2 \frac{R_f}{R_2}$$

provided that the following assumptions are made:

$$A \rightarrow \infty$$
$$Z_{in} \rightarrow \infty$$
$$I_{in} = 0$$

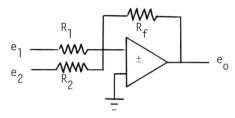

Figure 4: Voltage Summing Amplifier

Actually the gain A and input impedance of the amplifier is very high in practice and thus the assumptions are nearly valid.

This binary weighted resistor ladder technique can be expanded to produce 256 different voltage output levels using only eight resistors and an operational amplifier. It is important to note that the input voltages e_0 through e_7 in the diagram of figure 5, represent the output voltages 0 to 5 directly from the digital output port of the microcomputer.

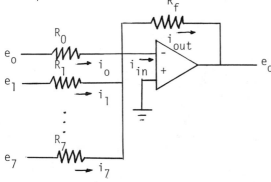

Figure 5: Binary Weighted Summing Network

Due to the fact that the input current i_{in} is approximately zero, then $i_{out} = i_0+i_1+i_2+i_3+...i_7$ or

$$i_{out} = \sum_{k=0}^{7} \frac{e_k}{R_k}$$

The output voltage is therefore

$$e_o = -R_f \sum_{R=0}^{7} \frac{e_k}{R_k}$$

If the value of the resistors are selected such that $R_0 = R$; $R_1 = 2R$; $R_2 = 4R$ through $R_7 = 128R$, then a formula may be developed as follows:

$$e_o = -\frac{R_f}{R} [\sum_{R=0}^{7} \frac{e_k}{2^k}]$$

The choice for R is a matter of judgment, for ideally, any value of R would be suitable. In practice a value of 10 kΩ would no doubt be appropriate based on the input impedance to the operational amplifier circuit in light of the digital I/O port output capabilities. The value to use for R_f should be based on full scale output requirements. If e_o full scale is to be 5 volts then $R_f = R$; if e_o full scale is to be 2.5 volts then $R_f = R/2$ and so forth.

$$e_o = \frac{-R_f E}{R} \sum_{R=0}^{7} \frac{B_k}{2^k}$$

where

$$B_k = 0 \text{ for "off"}$$

$$B_k = 1 \text{ for "on"}$$

$$E = 5 \text{ VDC}$$

One obvious disadvantage of this method is the lack of available resistors in this range. In addition, the input voltage accuracy and the resistor tolerance all affect the output.

It is desirable to employ a resistor network in the D/A conversion that does not use such a wide variation in values. A network of this type may be developed using the R-2R ladder network shown in figure 6.

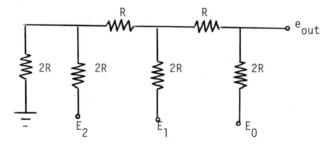

Figure 6: Simple R-2R Ladder Network

Employing the principle of superposition, it can be shown that if $E_1 = E_2 = 0$ then

$$e_o = \frac{E_o}{2}$$

if $E_o = E_2 = 0$ then

$$e_o = \frac{E_1}{4}$$

and if $E_o = E_1 = 0$ then

$$e_o = \frac{E_2}{8}$$

The fact that the voltages are binary weighted and that only two resistor values are used, makes this an ideal network for a D/A converter. It can be shown that for a network of eight input voltages, the R-2R ladder network output voltage becomes

$$e_0 = \sum_{i=0}^{7} \frac{E_i}{2^{i+1}}$$

where E_0 is the MSB and E_7 is the LSB.

It should be further pointed out that the output impedance of this network is always equal to R, regardless of the length of the ladder network. This is particularly useful when coupling this with an operational amplifier to provide scaling. In figure 7, the scale factor for this network would be

$$-\frac{R_f}{2R}$$

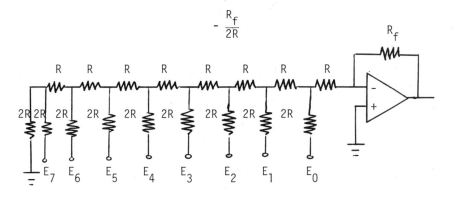

Figure 7: R-2R Digital to Analog Converter

Commercially available DACs may cost from $5 to $500 depending upon the number of bits of accuracy and the speed. A low cost unit is available from DATEL Systems Inc. The unit is an 8 bit converter and has a settling time of 600 nanoseconds. These circuits, although integrated, still require external components such as an op amp and/or diodes to be a totally functional D/A converter. These external components determine such factors as maximum output voltage, unipolar or bipolar operation, etc.

The D/A converter may be employed to perform a number of functions. For the purposes of this experiment, the D/A converter will be employed to generate a triangular waveform as shown in figure 8. Using the delay routine as previously developed, the step size may be easily programmed. The flowchart for this procedure is shown in figure 9.

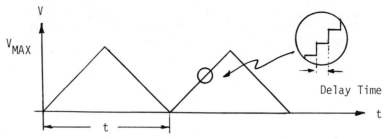

Figure 8:   Triangular Waveform

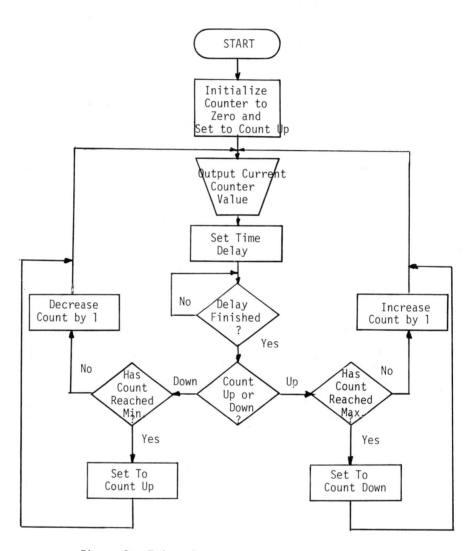

Figure 9:   Triangular Waveform Generation Program

Prelaboratory Investigation

1. Compare the various methods discussed for D/A conversion as to

   a) accuracy

   b) resolution

   c) cost

   d) hardware required

2. Select one of the D/A converter circuits discussed and implement it on a breadboard.

3. Write the program of figure 9.

4. It is desired to generate a triangular waveform with the following characteristics:

   a) $f = 20$ Hz

   b) $V_{MAX} = 5$ volts.

   Adjust the parameters of the program above to generate this waveform.

5. Write a program which will graph the data stored in 1 k of successive memory locations on the oscilloscope. Provide a Y axis sweep signal for synchronization.

6. Devise a routine which will display a digital value stored in a memory location on a voltmeter. The routine should, using an appropriate scale factor, display the base 10 equivalent on the meter of the unsigned binary number.

Laboratory Investigation

1. Determine the settling time for the circuit of step 2 of the prelaboratory investigation.

2. Verify the correct operation of the program from step 4 of the prelaboratory investigation.

3. Determine the maximum frequency for the triangular waveform program, experimentally.

4. Using the routine of step 5 of the prelaboratory investigation, graph the contents of 1 k of successive RAM memory locations with the data that they contain on initial power-up.

155

5. Verify the correct operation of the program from step 6 of the pre-laboratory investigation.

6. How can the program above be modified to produce output for signed binary values?

Questions for Further Study

1. How would it be possible to generate a sinusoidal waveform without storing it in memory? What type of formulas or techniques would be appropriate?

2. Survey the market for D/A converters and determine:

   a) cost

   b) speed

   c) resolution

   for at least three units currently on the market.

3. Draw a flowchart for a program which will display the sum of two signed binary numbers on a voltmeter.

4. List as many specific applications as possible for the D/A converter in consumer electronics.

5. Explain the following terms associated with a D/A converter:

   a) monotonic

   b) offset error

   c) settling time

   d) resolution

Experiment 27

ANALOG TO DIGITAL CONVERSION TECHNIQUES

Purpose

The purpose of this experiment is to investigate various methods for performing analog to digital conversion.

Background Investigation

An understanding of the total system is important if any micro-processor application is to be successful. Because so many of the input signals are analog by nature, this understanding must include A/D, analog to digital, conversion methods. A wide variety of applications include some technique of A/D conversion. Digital voltmeters, process control systems, hybrid computer systems and even voice analysis systems incorporate these converters. The most common application would be coupling an analog transducer to a microprocessor based system.

The principle of operation of these A/D converters is based on a sampling of an input signal. This analog voltage level is then converted to a digital word and subsequently processed by the computer. Consider the waveform shown in figure 1. Because the A/D conversion process requires finite time to complete, the sampled waveform should remain at a fixed voltage during the conversion interval such as Δt_1 and not as Δt_2. In cases where the sampled waveform rapidly changes and a slower A/D converter is employed, a sample and hold circuit is used to keep the voltage

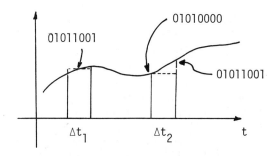

Figure 1: Sampling of an Analog Waveform

to be converted constant as shown by the dashed line portion above t_2.
The most appropriate sample is the one taken at the start of a conversion cycle.

Although many methods exist for performing the conversion process,
only six will be presented here.

1. Analog to Frequency Conversion

2. Analog to Pulse Width Conversion

3. Flash Conversion

4. Successive Approximation

5. Single Slope

6. Dual Slope

The first three methods are of the open loop type; no feedback is
provided during the conversion process. The last three all employ
some type of feedback.

In analog to frequency conversion, the analog input voltage v_a is
applied to a voltage to frequency converter. The variable frequency
output is subsequently converted to a digital word by a counter. The
counter circuitry and gating signal are similar to a commercially
available frequency counter, except the outputs are given in pure
binary rather than converted to information for a seven segment display.
The diagram for this configuration appears in figure 2.

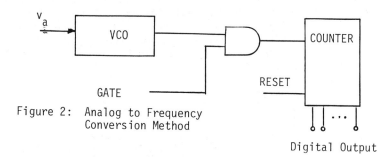

Figure 2: Analog to Frequency
Conversion Method

Digital Output

The conversion process begins by application of a RESET signal to
the counter circuit causing all digital outputs to be set to zero.
When a voltage, v_a, is applied to the voltage controlled oscillator, a
pulse train is produced where the frequency is proportional to v_a. The
GATE signal then allows the pulse train to be presented to the counter
for a precise period of time. The resulting count is proportional to
the voltage v_a. Although this is a relatively simple technique, it is
extremely slow and lacks the desired accuracy necessary in most digital

systems.

The analog to pulse width conversion method is similar to the one above but the gating signal is applied by the pulse width converter shown in figure 3. The frequency presented to the counter is obtained from an external clocking circuit. This somewhat relieves the problems of nonlinear VCDs and provides a more stable pulse train for the counter network.

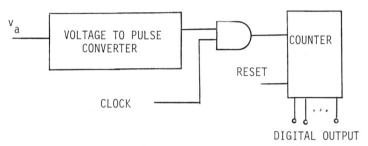

Figure 3: Analog to Pulse Width Converter

Both of the above techniques have shortcomings in precision and conversion time due to their designs. Faster and more precise methods exist, such as the one covered next.

The flash A/D converter makes use of various comparators and a reference voltage to perform the conversion. The comparators monitor the analog voltage and switch on when the voltage reaches a predetermined level. In the converter shown in figure 4, comparator one will turn on when the applied voltage $v_a > V_{REF}/4$, two when $v_a > V_{REF}/2$ and so forth.

The table which accompanies the figure shows the comparator outputs for various input voltages, v_a. The encoding logic is necessary to convert the comparator outputs to the desired binary configuration. A simple combination logic network is all that is required; however, a ROM may be employed to perform this function.

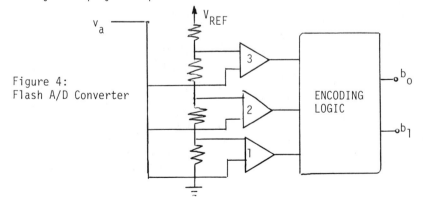

Figure 4:
Flash A/D Converter

159

	c_1	c_2	c_3	b_1	b_0
$v_a < 1$	0	0	0	0	0
$v_a > 1$	1	0	0	0	1
$v_a > 2$	1	1	0	1	0
$v_a > 3$	1	1	1	1	1

The name of this converter is derived from the fact that the conversion process is extremely high speed and is limited only by the longest propagation delay of the encoding logic and the corresponding comparator. It is also sometimes called a simultaneous A/D converter. The most obvious drawback of this type is the large number of components required. In addition to the resistors and encoding network, 2^n-1 comparators are required. For an eight bit converter, 255 comparators would be required. The flash converter is available in a total integrated form from several manufacturers. It should be used when speed is important.

The first of the feedback type A/D converters to be investigated is the successive approximation method. The diagram for this unit is shown in Figure 5. The converter employs a D/A converter in its design.

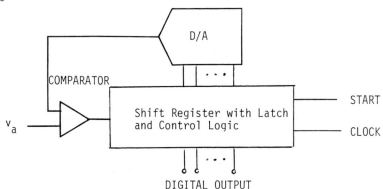

DIGITAL OUTPUT

Figure 5: Successive Approximation Converter

When the conversion process begins, the most significant bit of the shift register is set to one. The output voltage from the D/A converter is then compared to the unknown v_a. If the output of the D/A is less than v_a, the MSB is left at one; if not, it is set to zero. While the MSB is still set to this value, the next bit is tested. If the output of the D/A converter is now greater than v_a, the bit is set to zero; if not, the bit is set to one. This process continues until all bits are tested. The first, most significant, bit will produce an output $V_{MAX}/2$. The second produces an output $V_{MAX}/4$ until the final, least significant, bit in an eight bit word will produce an output $V_{MAX}/128$.

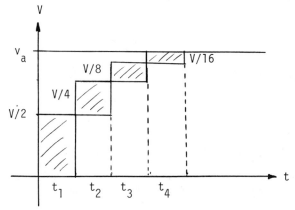

Figure 6: Typical Four Bit A/D Conversion where v_a = 15V/16

The process requires only eight tests to completely determine the equivalent digital word. Therefore, the speed characteristics are good and conversion times of from 100 kHz to 1 MHz can be expected. The successive approximation shift register and clocking circuitry would be relatively easy to implement in hardware logic. Even so, these could be programmed through a digital I/O port of the microprocessor system. It is assumed that the analog voltage v_a is constant during the conversion process. If this is not true or can not be determined, a sample and hold amplifier may be added on the input side and triggered when the conversion process is initiated.

A single slope A/D converter may be constructed as shown in figure 7. The ramp source may be an operational amplifier connected as an integrator. When the ramp signal is reset, it will begin to rise from zero. The binary (or BCD) counter will begin to count and continue until the input voltage v_a and the ramp voltage v_R are equal. The conversion is then completed and the counter output latched.

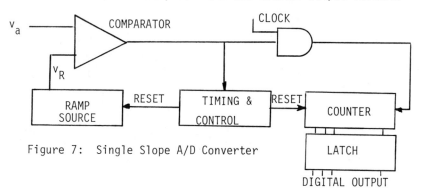

Figure 7: Single Slope A/D Converter

161

The counter may count in either binary or BCD because the output is not fed back through a D/A converter as in the successive approximation type. This makes it ideally suited for BCD based test instruments. The ramp source, external clock and timing unit, however, are critical components in the system.

Figure 8:
Typical Single
Slope Operation

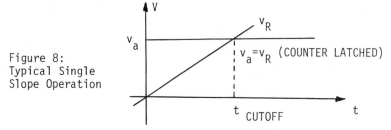

The dual slope A/D converter is similar to the single slope version but is slower in operation due to the added ramp function generated. Two transmission gates are employed to allow switching between the input voltage v_a and the reference voltage V_{REF}.

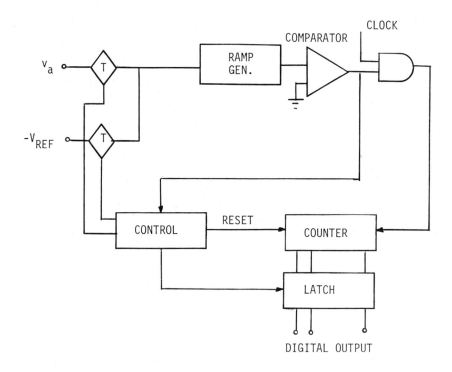

Figure 9: Dual Slope A/D Converter

The ramp generator produces a ramp based on the applied input voltage v_a for a period of time as determined by the CONTROL unit. When the time has elapsed, the control unit then switches the input of the ramp generator to V_{REF}. The clock and binary or BCD counters are then enabled and allowed to count. When the ramp again reaches zero, the output of the counter is latched. The value of R and C in the ramp generator determine the slope of the ramp function generated.

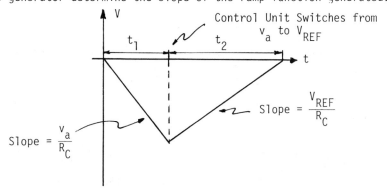

Figure 10: Dual Slope A/D Operation

In practice, the value of R and C do not enter into the conversion process and only t_2 is representative of the applied voltage v_a.

$$\frac{v_a}{RC} t_1 = \frac{V_{REF}}{RC} t_2$$

Solving the above equation for t_2 gives

$$t_2 = \frac{(v_a) t_1}{V_{REF}}$$

Because V_{REF} and t_1 are fixed values then:

$v_a \propto t_2$ and also the counter value. This A/D converters is often employed due to its good accuracy.

Prelaboratory Investigation

1. Devise a program to perform the operation of the shift register, latch and control logic in the successive approximation scheme. Use this in conjunction with a D/A converter to construct an A/D converter.

163

2. Investigate a sample and hold circuit for use with the D/A converter above.

3. Select either the single slope or dual slope converters described in the background investigation, based on hardware availability, and use the microprocessor to replace as much of the logic as possible. Write the software for its operation.

4. When an A/D converter is used that is totally independent of the microprocessor system, flag bits are provided to control its operation or inform the processor as to the status of the conversion underway. Typical names for these flag bits are given below. Describe briefly their meaning with respect to the converter.

   a) DONE   c) READY   e) OVER-RANGE

   b) BUSY   d) START

5. Design a two bit flash A/D converter similar to the one shown in figure 2. It should have a maximum input voltage of four volts. Using Karnaugh mapping techniques, minimize the encoding logic.

Laboratory Investigation

1. Determine the maximum rate at which an A/D conversion may be accomplished using the successive approximation scheme discussed in step 1 of the prelaboratory analysis.

2. Construct a table of input voltages (v_a) versus digital output for each of the converters constructed.

3. Which of the converters constructed will have the best conversion time?

4. Explain how the dual slope converter overcomes the problems of the single slope unit.

5. Using an attenuator network, double the range of the converter described in step 1 above.

6. Determine the conversion time for the flash A/D converter designed in step 5 of the prelaboratory investigation.

Questions for Further Study

1. For the dual slope converter, assuming R = 20 kΩ and C = .05 μf, what will the slopes be if v_a = 5 volts and V_{REF} = -10?

2. How long will the conversion take if the clock frequency is 1 MHz?

3. Construct a table of advantages and disadvantages for each of the A/D converters discussed in this experiment.

4. If the output of the V_{CO}, for the system shown in Figure 2, is 10 kHz to 100 kHz for a v_a of 0 to 10 V, what would be a reasonable gate time to insure an accurate conversion?

5. Devise a simple scheme to perform A/D conversion on several input signals using only one A/D converter.

6. If an eight bit successive approximation A/D converter with a conversion range of 0 to 10 V is used to convert a 5.89 volt signal, what would be the binary output?

AN AUTORANGING DIGITAL VOLTMETER

Purpose

In this experiment the principles of microprocessor control of
test instruments will be covered by investigating an autoranging
digital voltmeter.

Background Investigation

Many test instruments employ a microprocessor to control their
function. Digital multimeters are available to read voltage, current
and resistance and some even have an ability to perform calculations
based on the input voltage readings. This allows the meters to read
directly other quantities. For example, a pressure transducer may
output a voltage proportional to the pressure in a hydraulic system.
A proportionality constant is all that is needed to adjust the reading
to give PSI directly. Further refinements in these instruments will
allow them to easily adapt to any environment.

A simple autoranging digital voltmeter will be presented in this
experiment to give the novice some additional insight into the applications in the test instruments area. Additional software will be all
that is needed to make this a super intelligent device capable of
reading transducer outputs directly in other units such as PSI, flow,
velocity, etc.

As in most units, the output will be displayed in BCD on seven
segment displays. A typical voltmeter may have an output display
similar to:

$$+ \quad 1.888$$
$$- \quad 1.8.8.8.$$

This type of display is referred to as a 3 1/2 digit display. The
number of digits displayed is a direct result of the accuracy of the
A/D converter used and the number of bits used for the output. In
the above example, without multiplexing, 18 output bits would be re-
quired--one each for the decimal places, the leading 1 and the sign,
and four each for the three seven segment displays. Multiplexing of
the decimal points and display values could reduce the number of bits
to ten. Such a multiplexing scheme could easily be employed if a

display specifically designed for this purpose were employed. Ripple blanking can be used to suppress leading zeros in the final display. The display shown could show values from .001 to 1999. This however may not be a true indication of the accuracy of the A/D converter.

Depending on the number of bits of significance of the A/D converter, the cost of the unit and the precision that can be expected, the output display may contain fewer digits. If the A/D converter employed is set to operate in the bipolar mode and has eight bits of significance, then the range of output values will be

+2.54 to -2.56

with a 20 mv per bit operation. If it is configured to operate in the unipolar mode, then the range will be

0 to 5.10 volts

Actually, the A/D converter may be scaled to operate in any fashion and the output can easily be set to read 0 to 10.20 volts using a 40 mv per bit precision. Two eight bit ports or a single 16 bit port can be used with 16, 12 or 10 bit A/D converters to provide greater precision. For the purposes of this experiment, it will be assumed that an A/D converter is employed with the following resolution:

10 bits $\Rightarrow$ 1024 combinations $\Rightarrow$ 0 to 10.23 volt range

The display used for this circuit will appear as follows:

Because the possibility of negative voltages is not allowed, the negative sign will not be used. In this portion of the experiment, the possibility of over range values will also not be allowed and thus the decimal point will be permanently on at the position indicated.

It is a simple matter to construct a hardware interface diagram for this problem. It is shown in figure 1.

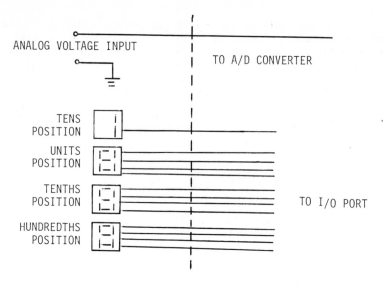

ANALOG VOLTAGE INPUT

TO A/D CONVERTER

TENS
POSITION

UNITS
POSITION

TENTHS
POSITION

HUNDREDTHS
POSITION

TO I/O PORT

Figure 1:   Simple Voltmeter Application

The precision of this simple voltmeter will be 10 mv per bit,
making the display the appropriate size. The software for this process
is left to the reader. The entire procedure would consist of conversion of the input A/D bit configuration to the appropriate BCD values
for the display.

A/D converters often indicate over range by displaying all ones
in the accumulator upon completion of the conversion process. These
converters can safely handle voltages considerably higher than the
maximum readable value. For example, a converter with a maximum voltage of 10 volts can handle 75 volts without damage. Voltage divider
networks such as the one shown in figure 2, under microprocessor control, can step down the voltage.

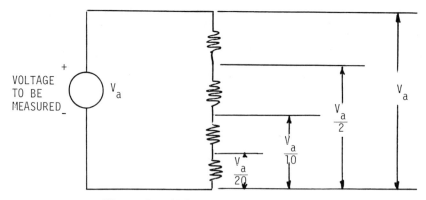

VOLTAGE
TO BE
MEASURED

V_a

$\frac{V_a}{20}$

$\frac{V_a}{10}$

$\frac{V_a}{2}$

V_a

Figure 2:   Voltage Divider Network

If the voltage V_a is less than or equal to 10 volts, it may be measured directly. If it is less than 50 volts, it may be measured by $\frac{V_a}{2}$ terminal, etc. The table below shows readings for different voltage inputs.

V_a	V_a	$V_a/2$	$V_a/10$	$V_a/20$
10	READ	UNDER	UNDER	UNDER
40	OVER	READ	UNDER	UNDER
60	OVER	OVER	READ	UNDER
100	OVER	OVER	READ	UNDER
140	OVER	OVER	OVER	READ

The procedure for enabling the appropriate voltage divider resistor would be as follows:

1. Enable $V_a/20$ and check for an over range condition.

   (If the maximum permissible voltage to the A/D converter is 75 volts, then damage can be prevented if V_a < 1500 volts.)

2. Continue to step up the voltage until an over range is detected.

3. The proper scale factor is one less than the over range reading.

Once the proper scale has been detected, the process reverts to selecting the appropriate decimal point, and formatting in input binary numbers to BCD for subsequent display. Selection of the appropriate divider resistor can be accomplished by using a solid state relay and controlling the selection by the microprocessor output port.

Prelaboratory Investigation

1. Draw a flowchart for the simple single scale voltmeter previously discussed using either a multiplexed or non-multiplexed display.

2. Code the flowchart into machine language.

3. Design a total hardware interface diagram for the autoranging voltmeter previously discussed. What precautions must be taken so that the A/D converter will not be damaged?

4. Draw a flowchart for the autoranging problem. Be sure the procedure will always return to $V_a/20$ in the idle state. Why?

5. Code the program for this procedure.

Laboratory Investigation

1. Using an appropriate procedure, check the operation of the hardware interface independent of the program for the single range voltmeter.

2. Verify the correct operation of the single range meter.

3. Independently test the autorange hardware interface.

4. Complete the testing of the entire system taking care not to damage the A/D converter.

Questions for Further Study

1. Briefly discuss a procedure for measuring currents using the voltmeter in this experiment.

2. How can resistance measurements be made?

3. Why are analog meters still popular?

4. What provision can be made so that both digital and analog readings can be taken?

Experiment 29

A DIGITAL CAPACITANCE METER

Purpose

The purpose of this experiment is to construct a digital
capacitance meter employing a 555 timer integrated circuit.

Background Investigation

A 555 timer chip has many applications in the microprocessor area.
It may act as the system clock or as an external timing generator to
produce interrupts at predetermined intervals. A little known application of this device can actually be used to produce a waveform whose
output frequency is proportional to capacitance.

The diagram given in figure 1 shows how the 555 may be connected
as an astable multivibrator. The external capacitor charges through
R_A and R_B but discharges through R_B only.

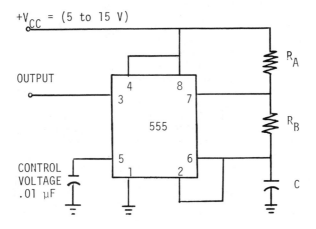

Figure 1: 555 as an Astable Multivibrator

The capacitor shown in figure 1 charges between 1/3 V_{CC} and 2/3 V_{CC}. Because the trigger level is also proportional to the supply voltage, the output frequency of this circuit is independent of the supply.

It can be shown that the period of the output waveform is:

$$T = 0.693(R_A + 2R_B)C$$

or
$$T \propto C$$

for fixed values of R_A and R_B. If the period of the waveform is known then the value of the capacitor may be easily determined. In an application of this type it may be a good idea to use precision components for R_A and R_B to insure the proper accuracy. The graph in figure 2 shows various operating points for the astable configuration. Actually, the 555 will operate over wider frequency ranges than that shown in the graph. For cases such as this, the equation may prove to be more useful.

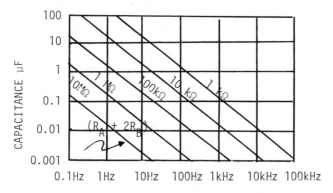

FREE RUNNING FREQUENCY

Figure 2: Operating Characteristics of the 555

At first glance, the equation for capacitance may look somewhat difficult to program. But if the units are appropriately discarded, the task becomes somewhat easier.

$$T = 0.693(R_A + 2R_B)C$$

If $R_A + 2 R_B$ is chosen to be 100 kΩ, using the graph, values of C between .001 and 100 μf can be measured. Then,

$$T = 0.693(100 \text{ k}\Omega)C$$

$$C = \frac{T}{0.693(100 \text{ k}\Omega)}$$

If T is assumed to be in milliseconds and C microfarads then

$$C = \frac{T}{(0.693)(100)}$$

$$C = \frac{T}{69.3}$$

still somewhat difficult to program.

Assuming T has units of 10^{-7} seconds, then

$$C = \frac{7}{693}$$

where C has units of nanofarads and the output of C will be from 1 to 100,000 nanofarads. The display could read

XXX.XXX

where the decimal point is permanently on, thus giving the illusion of reading microfarads.

A successive subtraction routine could be used to perform the division in a double or triple precision operation depending on the precision desired. The output of this device can be on a seven segment display and a single I/O bit may be used to measure input frequency. In fact, interrupts may be used to provide the on-off action for the internal microprocessor timing loop.

Prelaboratory Investigation

1. Develop the hardware interface diagram for the digital capacitance meter.

2. Draw a flowchart for the algorithm needed to convert the measured period T into the corresponding value of C.

3. Write the complete program to measure the value of C and output it in microfarads on a seven segment display.

Laboratory Investigation

1. Test the hardware interface for the digital capacitance meter. Use a frequency counter to determine the appropriate output for different values of C.

2. Test the equation to insure the accuracy and precision desired.

3. Verify the correct operation of the entire system by measuring precision capacitors over the designed range of the system.

4. Verify that the capacitors measured are within the precision specified.

Questions for Further Study

1. Using the specifications for the 555 timer element and precision, 1%, resistors, mathematically determine the accuracy of the measured values of C.

2. Can the 74121 be used in a similar manner to measure values of C?

3. How can values of inductance be measured using the same principle with slightly more hardware? (Hint: An AC impedance bridge can be employed.)

4. How can a digital ohmmeter be devised using the microprocessor?

Experiment 30

DATA TERMINAL INTERFACES

Purpose

The purpose of this experiment is to investigate the various interfaces, types of data terminals and the ASCII code used in data communications.

Background Investigation

Various codes have been developed for data transmission. Obviously, when the data is totally numeric, the codes used may be binary, BCD, gray, excess 3, etc. When alphanumeric data is to be transferred however, an expanded code is required. The code should have a unique bit configuration for each character and should be standardized. Three popular codes have been developed. The Baudot, the EBCDIC and the ASCII code are all used. The most popular of these codes, however, is the ASCII code. ASCII stands for the American Standard Code for Information Interchange.

The ASCII code is fundamentally composed of seven bits which provide for a total 128 different combinations. This code provides for all the letters of the alphabet, both upper and lower case, special characters, numbers and control functions. A table describing the code appears below.

$b_3b_2b_1b_0$ \ $b_6b_5b_4$	000	001	010	011	100	101	110	111
0000	NUL	DLE	SP	0	@	P	`	p
0001	SOH	DC1	!	1	A	Q	a	q
0010	STX	DC2	"	2	B	R	b	r
0011	ETX	DC3	#	3	C	S	c	s
0100	EDT	DC4	$	4	D	T	d	t
0101	ENQ	NAK	%	5	E	U	e	u
0110	ACK	SYN	&	6	F	V	f	v

$b_3b_2b_1b_0$ \ $b_6b_5b_4$	000	001	010	011	100	101	110	111
0111	BEL	ETB	´	7	G	W	g	w
1000	BS	CAN	(	8	H	X	h	x
1001	HT	EM	)	9	I	Y	i	y
1010	LF	SUB	*	:	J	Z	j	z
1011	VT	ESC	+	;	K	[	k	{
1100	FF	FS	,	<	L	\	ℓ	
1101	CR	GS	-	=	M	]	m	}
1110	SO	RS	.	>	N	^	n	∿
1111	SI	US	/	?	O	_	o	DEL

TABLE 1: The ASCII Code

The code is a seven bit code as previously stated. In most micro-computer applications however, an eight bit code is used due to the eight bit word length. In this variation, the eighth bit is always set to one. In still other variations, the eighth bit is reserved for parity. Take, for example, the numbers 1, 2, and 3 as shown in the table.

Character	7 Bit Code	8 Bit Code (No Parity)
1	0 110 001	10 110 001
2	0 110 010	10 110 010
3	0 110 011	10 110 011

If parity is employed, the words become:

1	10 110 001	00 110 001
2	10 110 010	00 110 010
3	00 110 011	10 110 011

In the parity words above, the eighth bit is always set to yield the appropriate parity. In the case of even parity, the value of the eighth is such that the number of ones in the word will always be even. These parity bits are used in error detection based on the assumption that only one bit in any word may be in error.

The ASCII code is easy to use when inputting numbers. A quick check of the table shows that the hex equivalent of each of the codes is 31, 32, 33, 34...etc. By simply removing the leading 4 bits, it is possible to obtain the binary equivalent of the number. This may be accomplished in one of two ways: 1) subtract 30_H from the code; 2) mask out the high order bits by ANDing with $0F_H$. The latter technique does not depend on parity or whether the code is seven bit or eight bit.

ASCII data transmission can be a serial or parallel format. The parallel format usually lessens the amount of hardware required for interface but requires the input/output device to be in close proximity to the computer due to the number of wires that must connect the two. The serial method, although considerably slower, does not require this massive hook-up. Software or external hardware must be employed to convert the parallel data to the serial format. Due to the human operator, speed is not usually a concern when making the decision of which form to use. The fact that data communication devices are often used over the phone lines does, however, dictate the serial method. An example of a parallel operated keyboard input device will exhibit some of the aspects of data communications and therefore a good place to begin further investigation.

Consider the ASCII encoded keyboard shown in figure 1. The strobe and timing logic continually scans the entire keyboard waiting for a key depression. The data lines d_0 to d_6 contain the data output from this scanning. It is constantly changing. When a key is depressed, a signal is sent to the strobe circuit that latches the ASCII code for that key into the latching network. Thus, d_0 to d_6 contain the seven bit ASCII code. The line, d_7, then indicates that valid data is present. The data will remain latched until a signal informs the keyboard that the data has been received. Once the signal is received, the logic will resume strobing the keyboard in search of another character.

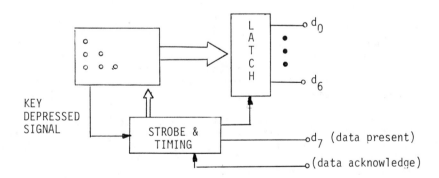

Figure 1: Keyboard Logic

The software for this procedure is somewhat simplified due to the fact that the eighth bit, d_7, of the input data word is the strobe bit. The flowchart for this procedure is given below in figure 2.

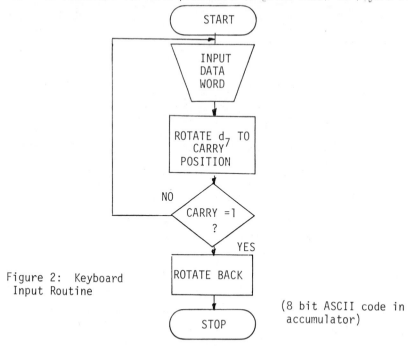

Figure 2: Keyboard Input Routine

(8 bit ASCII code in accumulator)

Before the serial format data transmission for a keyboard and printer is investigated, additional terminology must be introduced. Thse terms are simplex, half duplex and full duplex. Simplex implies that data may be transmitted in one direction only while duplex means that data may be transmitted in both directions. Most peripheral communications schemes utilize the duplex mode.

Duplex is further broken down into half and full. These terms primarily have to do with the echo back character printed as a result of a keystroke. In the half duplex mode, when a key is depressed, it is sent to the computer system and the character typed is also automatically printed. Full duplex, on the other hand, does not produce this automatic echoed character. When a key is depressed, the character is sent to the computer system. If an echo character is to be produced, the computer must send it to the printer.

There are advantages to both systems. The half duplex mode requires less computer time because the computer is relieved of the responsibility of outputting the echo character. In the full duplex mode an error in transmission may be detected more easily if the typed character is not the same as the echoed character. In addition, in computer systems that require a password for entry, the echo may be

turned off during that portion of data transfer. Most terminals have
the capability of operating in either mode. A double character
printed every time a key is depressed may indicate the terminal is
operating in a half duplex mode while the software assumes a full
duplex terminal.

The hardware serial to parallel data conversion is accomplished
in the I/O portion of the computer system. This data communication
is done asynchronously, that is, the characters are transmitted one
at a time in a random sequence to the printer or received from the
keyboard. Handshaking or control lines to the device inform the CPU
when it is ready to transmit or receive data. This device is called
a UART (Universal Asynchronous Receiver Transmitter) and is respon-
sible for control and data transmission. A block diagram of this
device and its interconnection to the rest of the computer unit is
shown in figure 3.

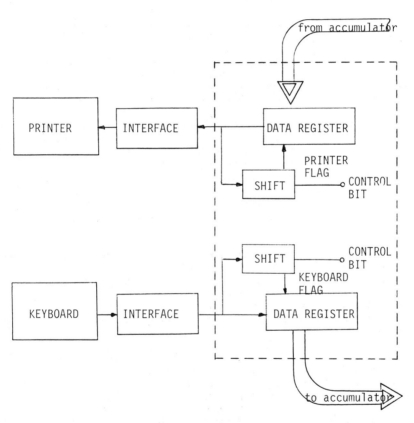

Figure 3: UART Logic

The operation of the UART may be explained as follows. When a character is to be transmitted to the printer, it must first be loaded into the accumulator. A parity bit may be added at this time to make the ASCII coded word compatible with the terminal in use. The character is then transmitted to the UART, usually via an I/O instruction, and subsequently transmitted serially to the printer. The serial transmission begins with a start bit (always low but not part of the data word) to properly synchronize the printer and the UART. The data is then shifted out of the register. At the end of the character, two stop bits, always high, are transmitted. (The number of stop bits may vary). In this application, a total of 11 bits are necessary to transmit a single character.

The data transmission of each character must be properly synchronized with the receiver. Data transmission takes place at a relatively low speed so that even though either the transmitter or receiver clock rate may drift slightly, it will still be sampled at the appropriate intervals. The characters themselves may be transmitted or received in an asynchronous manner even though the bits within a single character must be synchronous.

The speed at which data is transmitted is a function of the terminal used. If a terminal with a print speed of ten characters per second used an 11 bit word to transfer data, then the maximum bit transfer rate would be 110 bits per second or 110 baud.

When a character is received from the keyboard, the same procedure applies. The character originates at the keyboard in the form of 11 serial bits and is sent to the UART. Once the UART has shifted the character into the internal register, the 8 bit data character may be read into the accumulator.

If the terminal in use uses parity, a simple ORing with 80_H will cause the resulting data to be stored as eight bit no parity.

Because data transfer between the terminal and the UART must be done at a predetermined rate, handshaking or control lines are provided to insure that the UART is ready to receive or ready to transmit data. In figure 3, the status flag for the printer indicates the previous character has been printed and it is now ready to accept a new character. The status flag for the reader indicates that a character has been received and it is now ready to transfer data to the computer.

The printer and reader flags are usually connected to an I/O port independent of the data port and may be ready by an IN instruction. The printer flag is automatically busied (set to 1) whenever an output to the data port is done. It will return to a 0 when the operation is completed. The reader flag is readied (set to 0) when a valid character has been received by the UART. It will return to 1 when the ASCII code is inputted to the CPU.

If the user does not bother to check the condition of the status
flags before inputting or outputting, error conditions may occur.
These error message flags, generated by the UART, are usually part of
the status word. A typical form for the status word is as follows:

BIT POSITION	FUNCTION
0	Keyboard Status
1	Not Used
2	Parity Error
3	Framing Error
4	Data Overflow Error
5	Not Used
6	Not Used
7	Printer Status

Note the pointer status and keyboard status bits are located at the
ends of this word. This will ease the programming requirements by
requiring only one rotate instruction to place the bit into the carry
position for checking.

Other devices are available on the market for performing functions similar to the UART. One such device is the ACIA, Asynchronous
Communications Interface Adapter. Its function is essentially similar except data formats and rates are programmable. The baud rate is
adjustable over a limited range and the number of start, stop and data
bits is adjustable to suit most terminal requirements.

Referring again to figure 3, the interface devices represent
logic or interface levels that are required to match the terminal to
the computer. These interface levels may be 20 ma current loop,
RS-232C, RS-422 or RS-423. The RS-232C and 20 ma current loop interfaces are among the most common.

The 20 ma current loop is most often associated with a Model 33
Teletype [R] terminal, although some of these terminals may operate
with an RS-232 interface also. A simple circuit may be developed to
provide this interface. These are shown in figure 4. The opto-iso-
lation is necessary to isolate the Teletype electrically from the
microcomputer. The baud rate associated with the Model 33 is 110.

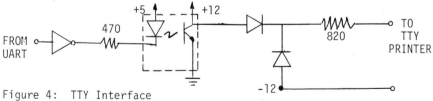

Figure 4: TTY Interface

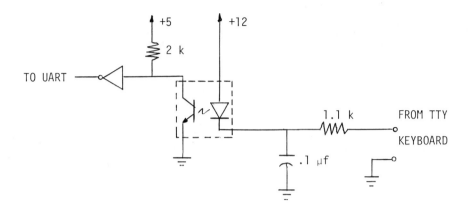

Figure 4: TTY Interface (Continued)

The RS-232C interface, by far the most popular, was originally
adopted as a standard by the Electronics Industry Association (EIA).
The standard covers handshaking signals used to control standard telephone equipment, and modems (modulator-demodulator) used to intercon-
nect computers and terminals over the telephone. There are also specifications given for the pin connections on a standard DB-25 pin con-
nector. This is done so that all terminals and modems are plug-in
compatible.

The standard pin connections and terms associated with these are:

Pin Number	RS-232C	Function
2	BA	Transmit Data
3	BB	Receive Data
5	CB	Clear to Send
6	CC	Data Set Ready
7	AB	Signal Ground
8	CF	Carrier Detect

Due to the fact that the standard covers connections from a terminal to a modem, when the terminal is connected directly to the computer, a connection called a null modem cable must be used. In this case, the computer thinks it is communicating with a modem and so does the terminal. The receive and transmit wires are crossed as shown below.

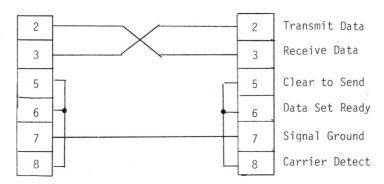

Figure 5: Null Modem Cable Connections

Typical interface levels for the RS-232C interface are shown in figure 6.

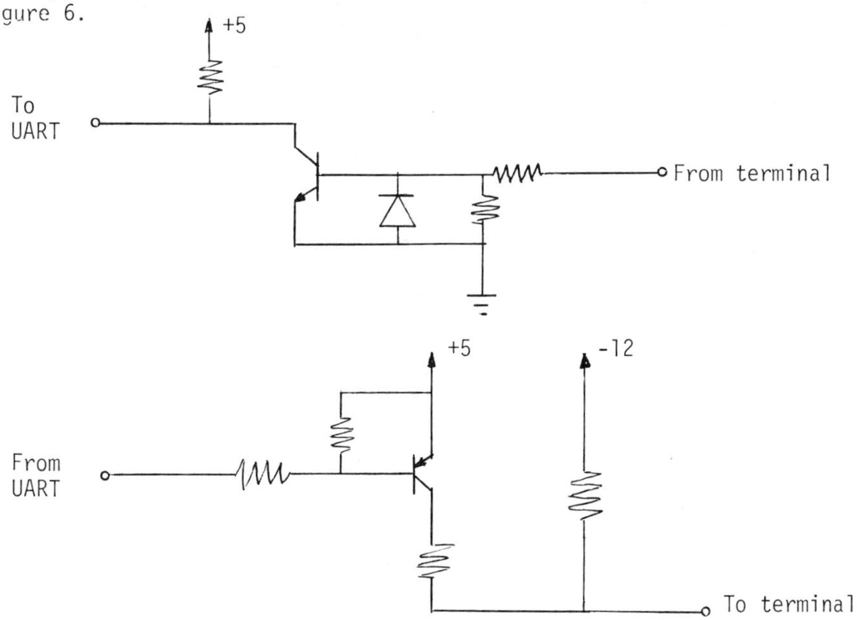

Figure 6: RS-232 Levels

183

Prelaboratory Investigation

1. Investigate the operation of your terminal in conjunction with the microcomputer system and answer the following questions:

    a) Baud rate

    b) Interface method

    c) Full or half duplex operation

2. When power is applied to the system initially, the state of the printer flag and keyboard flag are unknown. If, for example, the printer status is busy and nothing is being printed, it will never reset. What can be done by your program to insure the proper flag status?

3. Write a program so that the received ASCII codes may be displayed for examination either using an available memory location or a front panel display.

4. Devise a program to input 10 typed characters and store them in 10 successive memory locations. When the 10th character is inputted, generate a carriage return and a line feed and reprint all 10 characters.

5. Write a program to input 10 pairs of numbers and store them in memory in BCD format.

Laboratory Investigation

1. Determine the status of the printer and keyboard flags on power up. Are they predictable?

2. Using the program developed in step 3 of the prelaboratory investigation, determine:

    a) 7 bit or 8 bit ASCII code used

    b) Even, odd or no parity

3. Determine the ASCII codes for each of the following:

    a) A

    b) !

    c) CONTROL C

    d) Delete or rubout

    e) (

4. Verify the correct operation of the program from step 4 of the prelaboratory investigation.

5. Check the operation of the program from step 5 of the prelaboratory investigation.

Questions for Further Study

1. Often, when a system is operating in the full duplex mode, the printer flag is not checked before the echo character is sent to the UART. Why?

2. Which of the following are standard baud rates?

   9,600   1,200   110

   4,800   600   75

   2,400   300   50

3. The function of the UART may be completely done by software. Devise a program to perform this function.

4. What is the difference between a UART and a USART?

5. Can a UART be constructed using only common TTL logic gates? How?

6. If a terminal operates at 300 baud and has a print speed of 30 characters per second, describe the transmission format.

185

RANDOM NUMBER GENERATION

Purpose

In this experiment, procedures will be investigated for the generation of pseudo random numbers.

Background Investigation

There are many procedures that exist for the generation of random numbers. Some, however, will not pass the test of being truly random, random in the statistical sense. The internal registers of a micro-processor are said to power up in a random manner. Although they may vary from one chip to another, for a given microprocessor chip, the power up bit configurations are quite predictable.

A procedure to generate a random sequence of numbers is given below:

$$R_{i+1} = F(\pi + R_i)^5$$

If the fractional portion of the number R_i is taken on each iteration, the resulting values, between zero and one, will satisfy the statistical test. One must, however, choose the initial value R_0. If

$$R_0 = .1$$

then

$$R_1 = .925$$

$$R_2 = .309$$

etc.

The series will be exactly the same, if the initial value is always taken to be .1. This list is called pseudo random because of this fact. Non-pseudo random numbers usually do not require an initial guess, have procedures for randomizing the initial guess, or will not generate the same sequence regardless of the initial guess.

The above procedure does illustrate the procedure for generating random numbers, but because of the calculations required may not generate a true list of random values. Working with a set of integer numbers would greatly ease this problem.

Consider the numbers between 1 and 100. If any number in this list has equal likelihood of being chosen, then the result is considered to be random. One of the simplest procedures to generate such a list follows. The initial value is R_0 then,

$$R_{i+1} = C \ R_i \ MOD(B)$$

The procedure for finding the term $CR_i \ MOD(B)$ in the above equation is as follows.

$CR_i \ MOD(B)$ = the remainder of the largest integer multiple of B that is less than R_i is subtracted from R_i.

$$580 \ MOD(100) = 80$$

(The largest integer multiple of 100 that is less than 580 is 500. Hence, 580-500 = 80.)

Using this procedure and the following constants, the pattern of random numbers is given below.

$$R_0 = 4$$
$$R_1 = 6.4 \ MOD(99)$$
$$= 24$$
$$R_2 = 6.24 \ MOD(99)$$
$$= 45$$
$$R_3 = 6.45 \ MOD(99)$$
$$= 72$$
$$R_4 = 6.72 \ MOD(99)$$
$$= 36$$
$$R_5 = 6.36 \ MOD(99)$$
$$= 18$$

To test the series of random numbers generated, some of the procedures listed below may be applied.

1. The average of all the random numbers should be about the
   maximum value / 2 (99/2 in the case above).

2. The number of values generated that are divisible by 3
   should be about the maximum value / 3 (99/3 in the case
   above for 100 numbers).

3. The number of times a particular value repeatedly occurs
   in the list should be K/maximum value, where K is the
   total number of random values generated.

4. For L = 0,1,2,...9, the number of values between L/10
   times the maximum value and (L+1)/10 times the maximum
   value should be about K/10, where K is the total number
   of random values generated.

The values generated by this procedure are, again, pseudo random
numbers. Using the same set of initial values for R_0, C and B, the
same list of numbers would be generated. Additional procedures may be
developed for the generation of random numbers.

Prelaboratory Investigation

1. Program the procedure for the generation of pseudo random numbers
   as outlined in this experiment as a subroutine. Parameters for
   the routine (R_0, C and B) should be used as input.

2. Develop a main program which will generate a list of 100 numbers
   using the subroutine above.

3. A microprocessor based game is on the market which will generate
   a sequence of lights and require the player to repeat the sequence.
   Each time the player properly repeats the sequence, the processor
   adds one additional light to the pattern.

   a) Develop an interface for a four light and four button inter-
      face.

   b) Using the random number generator, program the processor to
      generate the light sequence and test the player input for
      the proper sequence.

Laboratory Investigation

1. Using the tests outlined in the background investigation and the
   following values, test the following to insure that the procedure
   will generate a list of truly random numbers:

a) $R_0 = 7$, B = 48, C = 3

b) $R_0 = 6$, B = 100, C = 5

c) $R_0 = 86$, B = 99, C = 7

2. Implement and test the microprocessor based game devised in step 3 of the prelaboratory investigation.

Questions for Further Study

1. How can the initialized guess be randomized using either software or an external hardware arrangement?

2. Can the randomness of this procedure be predicted based on R_0, C and B?

3. Because of the nature of the microprocessor, and the fact that it can easily be interfaced to external devices, how could the random number procedure be relegated to an external hardware circuit?

4. What is another simple software procedure that can be used to generate a random number list?

5. Other than microprocessor based games, what applications exist for the random number generator?

Experiment 32

SECURITY SYSTEMS

Purpose

The purpose of this experiment is to become familiar with hardware interfacing and microprocessor programming by developing a home security system.

Background Investigation

Investigation of microprocessor applications would not be complete without a look into the home/office security systems. Although the surveillance of a building is not an extremely time consuming task for the microprocessor, it is a job that can be done while the processor is not busy, or even be driven by interrupts so the processor can be free to do more demanding work. Environmental control systems for office buildings may also conduct the security surveillance in addition to performing other tasks.

In a normal environment, all doors, windows and access points should be wired to prevent intruders. In addition, a method of bypassing the system should be provided for authorized personnel.

To take full advantage of the decision making capability of the microprocessor, a system of this type may be designed to include the following characteristics:

1. All doors and windows will be serviced individually by normally closed contacts. (Closed windows indicate normally closed conditions.)

2. Bypass of the system is made via coded entry on a keypad available at the normal entry points.

3. Access to designated areas can be specified according to the time of day and various security codes to be entered at the keyboards.

4. Intrusion alarm will provide information, conveyed in an appropriate format, as to the point of intrusion.

5. Logging of entries and exits can be made on an appropriate

hardcopy terminal showing individual requesting access,
time of day and entry point.

   Additional options may be incorporated into the system depending
on the degree of sophistication desired. These would include fire
alarm system, auto-dial of police and fire, etc.

Prelaboratory Investigation

1. Devise a complete security system plan for a particular floor or
   room within the building you normally work. Investigate normal
   traffic patterns and necessary entry points.

2. Develop a hardware interface for this system showing contact types
   and locations as well as keyboard interface, real time clock interface and hardcopy device interface.

3. Flowchart the software needed for this system.

4. Code the software for this system.

Laboratory Investigation

1. Wire the interface for this system to simulate the actual operating conditions.

2. Test the hardware interface to insure its correct operation.

3. Make the appropriate tests for the entire system.

Questions for Further Study

1. Why should the contacts used to monitor door and window security
   be normally closed instead of normally open?

2. How could this system be revised to use interrupts?

3. Could the revised interrupt driven system be run independent
   and in addition to other microprocessor based applications?

Experiment 33

AUTOMOTIVE APPLICATIONS
THE DIGITAL TACHOMETER

Purpose

The purpose of this experiment is to investigate one particular application of microprocessors to automotive electronics.

Background Investigation

The semiconductor was first introduced into automotive systems in the mid-fifties. Since that time, electronics have played an ever increasing role in the operation and maintenance of today's car. A typical automobile can contain 20 electronic subsystems, a quarter mile of cable, 80 switches, 15 electric motors, 70 lamps and 25 sensors, fuse breakers and over 100 connections.

In 1977 the first microprocessor was introduced in the Oldsmobile Toronado as part of the spark plug timing circuit. Previously, engines ran "open loop" with little control over efficiency and operating conditions. The microprocessor will, in effect, close the loop and thereby provide lower emission levels and yet higher efficiency. In addition, the processor will still have enough "free time" to make operating the vehicle more pleasurable and provide valuable information to the driver.

The microprocessor will be delegated to perform such functions as:

Engine Control

Ignition and timing control

Cylinder selection

Fuel Management

Level indication

Consumption indicators

Electronic carburetion

Load Management and Transmission Control

Maintenance

    Vehicle service

    Self test diagnostics

Headlight Control

Braking Control

Power Control

    Voltage regulation

    Electronic power supply

Convenience

    Tachometer

    Speedometer

    Mobile communications

    Instrumentation

    Digital clock

Safety and Security

    Drunk-driving prevention

    Air bag actuator

    Combination ignition key

    Antitheft

    Low tire pressure indication

The digital tachometer is but one of the simpler applications of microprocessors to automotive electronics. Many individuals may prefer an analog type tachometer to a digital representation. However, a digital format may be useful in tune-up applications and other cases where a precise readout is required. An analog readout may be easily obtained from the same electronic sensors using an inexpensive D/A converter.

The type of transducer used for the pulse pickup may vary depending on cost, degree of accuracy required and type of engine. It will be assumed, for the purposes of this experiment, that the transducer will produce a 0 to 5 volt pulse. In order to fully exploit the intelligence of the microprocessor, the number of pulses per revolution should be programmable (1 to 8). In addition, the display should indicate revolutions per minute. For the purposes of this experiment, the display should be updated every second.

RPM may be determined from the following formula:

$$RPM = \frac{N_M}{P_R} \times 60$$

where   RPM is revolutions per minute

N_M is the number of pulses measured in one second

and P_R is the number of pulses per revolution as programmed.

Internal data representation should be in BCD and the procedure should produce readings of 0-100 revolutions per minute. A flowchart of the general procedure appears in figure 1. Interrupts are used to input the number of pulses measured during a given counting interval.

The generalized tachometer program flowchart appears in figure 1. The input pulse count is accepted via an interrupt routine. Every time a pulse occurs the storage location N_M is updated. Constant reinitialization of N_M every second by the main program insures that the value stored is the number of pulses per second. P_R is input to the main program every time it is initialized. The basic loop in the main program must comprise the one second delay. This includes the output routines and calculation of $N_M/P_R \times 60$.

The most difficult portion of the procedure to program is the calculation of RPM. The procedure can be somewhat more easily implemented if we take advantage of the structure of the formula and in particular the number 60.

$$N_M(60)_{10} = N_M(64)_{10} - N_M(4)_{10}$$

$$N_M(60_{10}) = N_M(100_8) - N_M(4_8) = N_M(74)_8$$

It is a simple matter to multiply N_M times 64 by rotating the number to the left six places. It would be a good idea to use double precision numbers at this point. N_M can then be multiplied times 4 by rotating to the left two places. The subtraction of $N_M(4)_{10}$ from $N_M(64)_{10}$ gives the desired result. The division by P_R can be done by the successive subtraction method since the range of P_R is only from 1 to 8. Conversion to BCD for ease of display, by a method previously discussed, completes this process.

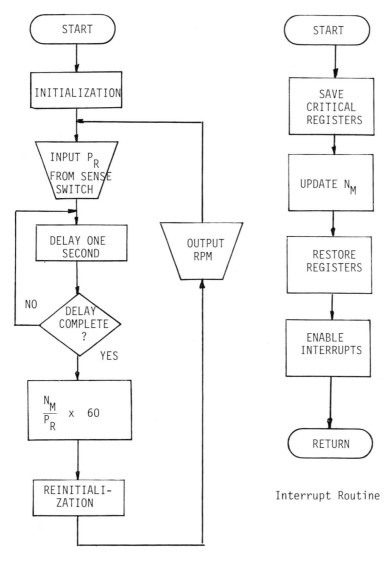

Background Program

Interrupt Routine

Figure 1: Generalized Tachometer Program

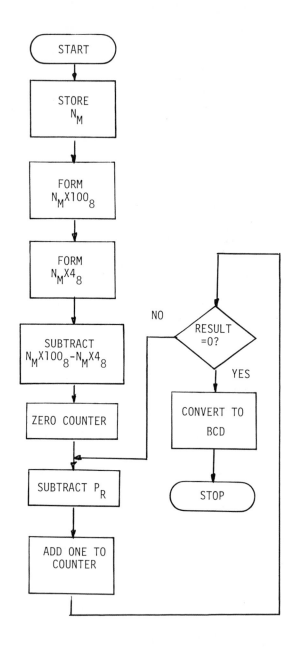

Figure 2: Specific Flowchart for $\dfrac{N_M \times 60_{10}}{P_R}$

Prelaboratory Investigation

1. Write the programs to implement the procedures outlined in the flowcharts shown in figures 1 and 2.

2. Answer the following questions regarding this procedure:

   a) Why were interrupts used in this procedure?

   b) Could this system be constructed without the use of interrupts?

   c) What, in your program, will affect the accuracy of the answer?

   d) What other procedure may be used to produce $N_M \times 60_{10}$?

Laboratory Investigation

1. Verify the correct operation by using a pulse generator to simulate the transducer output. Use various settings of P_R (1-8).

2. Determine the areas of inaccuracy and represent these in a graphical format. Explain these discrepancies.

3. Using the D/A converter and an analog voltmeter, construct an analog readout of the RPM indication.

Questions for Further Study

1. Assuming that the processor is "too busy" to perform the delay function in the main program and a one second external clock signal is available, how would the procedure be modified?

2. How could the tachometer program be slightly modified to produce a speedometer and indicate miles per hour?

3. Develop a conversion program such that the speedometer program output will indicate either miles per hour or kilometers per hour.

Experiment 39

TRAFFIC CONTROL

Purpose

The purpose of this experiment is to investigate the computer control of a traffic signal at a busy intersection.

Background Investigation

The microprocessor based traffic signal can be used to exemplify a feedback control system provided that a sensor is used to provide information regarding the awaiting cars or the flow through the intersection.

Sensing of the cars on each of the streets will be accomplished through the use of either pressure plates or inductance coils buried in the pavement. Although in an actual application of a four-way intersection, four sensors would be employed, they would operate in pairs and would be simply ORed together. A simple intersection of two one-way streets was chosen for the simulation, i.e., Milwaukee and State Streets (see figure 1).

To determine an appropriate algorithm, an investigation of the traffic flow should be conducted. In practice, this may yield a different result than the simulation in this experiment. For the purposes of this experiment, the following control criterion will be employed:

a) The light will be normally green to State Street and will operate for a minimum of 30 seconds regardless of the number of cars waiting on Milwaukee Street.

b) Once a car is sensed on Milwaukee Street and State Street has been green for at least 30 seconds, the lights will change and remain green on Milwaukee for 30 seconds.

c) If however, while the lights are green on Milwaukee, seven or more cars backup on State Street, the light will revert back to green on State after only a 10 second period.

d) A four second amber light will be employed in all light changes with an additional one second "all red" period.

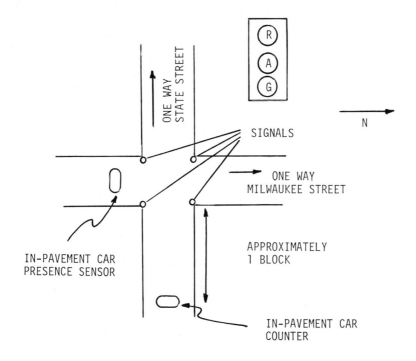

Figure 1: The Intersection of Milwaukee and State Streets

The traffic signals located on each corner would represent the
output of the controller. Figure 2 shows the hardware interface
diagram. Traffic signals are simulated by red-amber-green LEDs. The
debounced push buttons P_1 and P_2 simulate the sensors at both inter-
sections. To aid in counting the approaching cars to State Street,
an external hardware counter is provided. (The use of interrupts
would eliminate the need for this external hardware.)

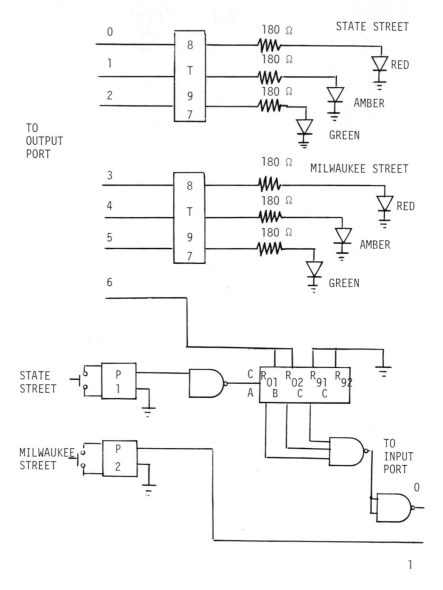

Figure 2: Digital Simulation of Street Control

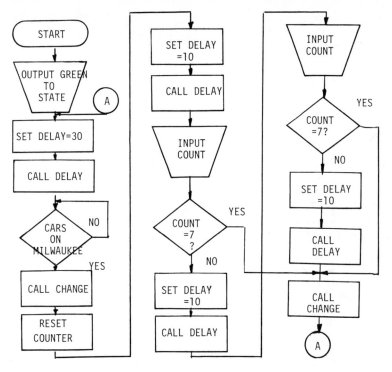

Figure 3: Generalized Flowchart

The generalized flowchart for this procedure appears in figures 3 and 4. The flowchart of figure 4 represents subroutines called by the main program.

Additional considerations in the design of systems such as this, could include:

a) time of day and traffic pattern fluxuations,

b) evening operation, such as flashing red in one direction and flashing yellow in the other,

c) emergency vehicle presence, steady red in all directions,

d) walk-don't walk signs,

e) multiple intersection control through the use of interrupt programming techniques.

Prelaboratory Investigation

1. Write the programs shown in the flowcharts of figures 3 and 4. It may be a good idea to reduce the time delays from 30 seconds to

201

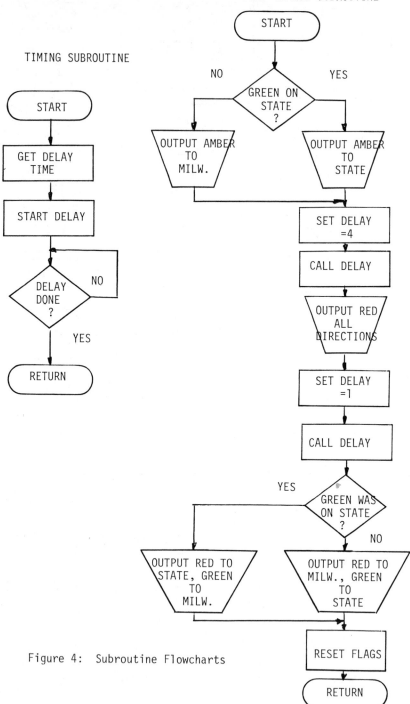

Figure 4: Subroutine Flowcharts

five seconds to facilitate debugging procedures.

2. Write a simple program to insure the hardware is properly func-
    tioning.

3. Redraw the flowchart for this program taking advantage of the
    interrupt facility.

Laboratory Investigation

1. Wire the hardware as shown in figure 2.

2. Verify the correct operation of the hardware only.

3. Verify the correct operation of the hardware and the software for
    the traffic light system.

Questions for Further Study

1. Discuss the major differences between the program outlined in the
    background investigation and a program that would take advantage
    of the interrupts.

2. List examples of other feedback control applications of the micro-
    processor.

3. A bridge is scheduled for destruction in three years because it
    has become incapable of supporting a full load of traffic. Block
    diagram a microprocessor based system that would employ a weight
    calculation system and traffic lights that would insure that the
    total weight on the bridge at any given time would not exceed a
    specified limit.

Experiment 35

REAL TIME DATA ACQUISITION

Purpose

The purpose of this experiment is to investigate a real time data collection system to monitor temperature fluctuations over a specified period of time.

Background Investigation

There are many systems available today that are employed to acquire, reformat and output data to some device. Such devices greatly reduce the need for operator intervention and provide an "automated" system, reducing errors. The flexibility of these systems has therefore been increased in recent years due to the microprocessor.

An example of a data acquisition system will be presented in this experiment. This sytem will be used to monitor temperature fluctuations in a given environment. It will be composed of the following hardware components:

1. temperature transducer,

2. A/D and D/A converters,

3. microcomputer,

4. oscilloscope

5. temperature display

The system will provide the basic monitoring functions and data storage system capabilities as described below:

1. monitor and display, on seven segment displays, the temperature continuously,

2. internal temperature representation should be in BCD format,

3. output, at a predetermined interval, the past history of the temperature fluctuations; a sample temperature should be taken X seconds (programmable) and a plot of the variations displayed continuously on the oscilloscope.

Optional:

Two set point temperatures (high and low) monitor the extreme variations and an alarm will sound when either of these variations are met.

The hardware interface diagram is shown in figure 1. The output of the temperature module provides a voltage that is proportional to temperature. The temperature transducer should be carefully selected so that the voltage varies linearly over the temperature range desired. In most cases, a calibration procedure should be followed to insure the desired accuracy is obtained.

Typically, an equation for resistance as a function of temperature for a transducer such as a thermister would be:

$$R = [5000+100(°F)]\Omega$$

An active network composed of operational amplifiers could be developed to provide a variable output voltage. In addition a bridge circuit could be used to provide this output. The 5000 and 100 terms in the equation may be modified if the temperature is to be in °C.

Since

$$°F = 9/5°C + 32$$

then

$$R = 5000 + 100 [9/5°C + 32]$$

$$R = [8200 + 180°C]\ \Omega$$

The oscilloscope display represents a continuous output of the history of the temperature over a prescribed period of time. The temperature may be displayed in a histogram format on the oscilloscope. The general flowchart for this procedure appears in figure 2.

Prelaboratory Investigation

1. Draw a more detailed flowchart for the procedure shown in figure 2. Subroutines written previously may be used, such as the binary to BCD conversions and the delay routines.

2. Design a temperature module, if one is not available, to conform to the specifications of the A/D converter and the thermister.

3. Write the complete program for the temperature monitor. Monitor the temperature variations every second for a period of 30 seconds and output this history on the oscilloscope.

4. Write a short routine to insure that the hardware interface shown in figure 1 is properly functioning.

5. Write the routine to monitor for an over or under temperature value. It should provide some alarm feedback when either of the two conditions occur.

Laboratory Investigation

1. Connect the temperature module as designed in step 2 of the prelaboratory investigation.

2. Calibrate this unit over the specified operating range.

3. Wire the interface diagram shown in figure 1 and test its operation with the program written in step 4 of the prelaboratory investigation.

4. Test the operation of the histogram program, the D/A converter and the oscilloscope portion independent of the remainder of the program by storing typical values in the appropriate memory location.

5. Test the entire program over the 30 second interval and simultaneously adjust the temperature.

6. Monitor the temperature fluctuations in the laboratory over a 30 second interval and simultaneously adjust the temperature.

Questions for Further Study

1. What are the alternatives to using an oscilloscope to display historical temperature values in this experiment?

2. What other means of monitoring the temperature and producing a voltage output are available? Are they cost effective?

3. State the accuracy of the recorded measurements in this experiment in $^{\circ}F$ or $^{\circ}C$.

4. List some typical applications of real time data acquisition from both the industrial and consumer markets.

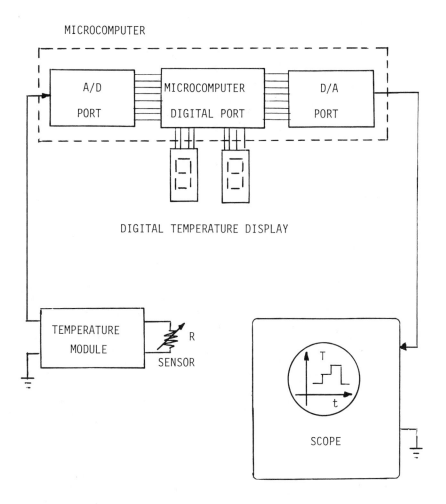

MICROCOMPUTER

A/D PORT

MICROCOMPUTER DIGITAL PORT

D/A PORT

DIGITAL TEMPERATURE DISPLAY

TEMPERATURE MODULE

R

SENSOR

T

t

SCOPE

Figure 1:   Hardware Interconnection Diagram

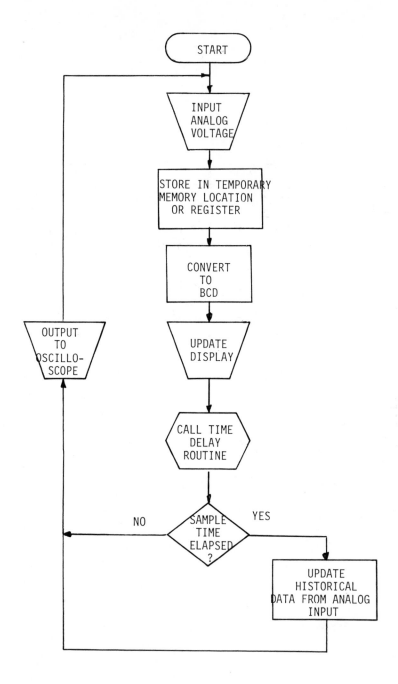

Figure 2: General Flowchart

208

Experiment 36

STEPPER MOTOR CONTROL

Purpose

The purpose of this experiment is to investigate the use of a microprocessor to control a stepper motor timing for a jog forward condition.

Background Investigation

Stepper motors have a variety of applications in industry from the control of a line printer and plotters to the construction of robots. Stepper motors respond to a command signal by moving in discrete increments instead of continuous motion like conventional motors. Step sizes can vary from 0.1° to 30° per step.

The stepper motor to be used in this experiment will increment in steps of 7.5 degrees in a direction determined by the application of a pulse supplied by the microprocessor to one of the four phases. If the applied pulses to the motor are in the sequence 0-1-2-3 (see figure 1) the motor will step in the forward direction.

Variable speeds are obtained by applying these signals at appropriately spaced intervals. This experiment will permit the speed of the motor to be varied as a function of the status of an I/O port.

A flowchart of the procedure for the operation of the stepper motor appears in figure 2. Due to the nature of the timing routine, a formula for the speed of the motor in steps per second can be determined to be:

$$\text{Steps per second} = \frac{1}{N\ (.0039)}$$

where N is the base 10 equivalent of the input port. For example, if all bits are high, the octal equivalent is 377_8 or 255_{10}, which results in a motor speed of 1 step/second.

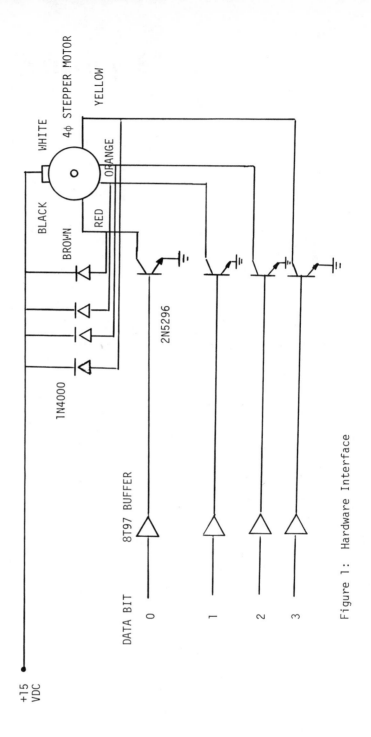

Figure 1: Hardware Interface

210

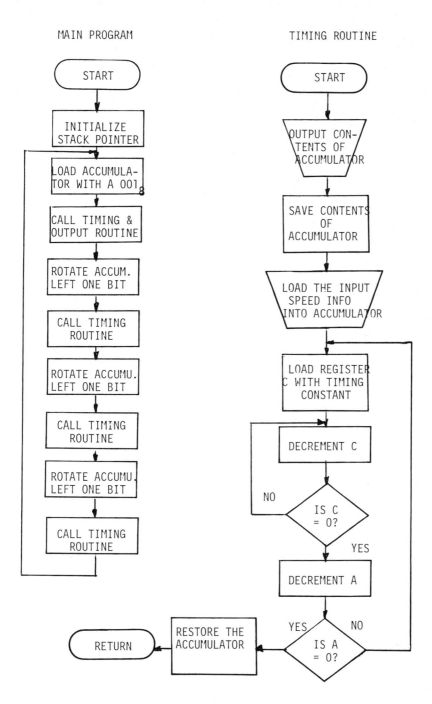

MAIN PROGRAM

START

INITIALIZE
STACK POINTER

LOAD ACCUMULA-
TOR WITH A 001₈

CALL TIMING &
OUTPUT ROUTINE

ROTATE ACCUM.
LEFT ONE BIT

CALL TIMING
ROUTINE

ROTATE ACCUMU.
LEFT ONE BIT

CALL TIMING
ROUTINE

ROTATE ACCUMU.
LEFT ONE BIT

CALL TIMING
ROUTINE

TIMING ROUTINE

START

OUTPUT CON-
TENTS OF
ACCUMULATOR

SAVE CONTENTS
OF
ACCUMULATOR

LOAD THE INPUT
SPEED INFO
INTO ACCUMULATOR

LOAD REGISTER
C WITH TIMING
CONSTANT

DECREMENT C

IS C
= 0?   NO

YES

DECREMENT A

IS A
= 0?   NO

YES

RESTORE THE
ACCUMULATOR

RETURN

Figure 2: Program Flowcharts

211

Prelaboratory Investigation

1. Write a short routine to test the hardware interface.

2. Write a program in machine language to implement the flowchart
    of figure 2. Verify this formula and the constant .0039 by
    comparing the instructions and the execution time.

3. Verify the correct operation of the interface circuitry using
    the program written in step 1 of the prelaboratory investigation.

4. Operate the program using the variable speed jogging program
    previously written.

5. Determine the slowest and fastest speed of this motor.

Questions for Further Study

1. List at least four specific applications of a stepper motor.

2. How was the equation:

$$\frac{1}{N\ (.0039)}$$

developed?

3. Determine the torque specifications of the stepper motor used
    in this experiment.

Experiment 37

COMPUTER TO COMPUTER COMMUNICATIONS

Purpose

In this experiment the basic types of inter-computer communications will be discussed and, in particular, parallel data communication.

Background Investigation

The low cost and availability of microprocessors have brought about a change in thinking when designing computer based equipment. It is often less expensive to design a system with multiple processors. The maze of wires interconnecting a stand alone processor and its peripheral devices is often more costly than making each device intelligent and using a single pair of wires for an interface.

Actually two, three or more processors may be interconnected to form an effective data communications network. Even large scale systems communicate to provide for remote diagnostics or data sharing networks. It is therefore not unreasonable to assume that a system designer may at one time or another be required to establish a protocol method for computer to computer communications.

Three basic forms of communications are obvious from a knowledge of microcomputer architecture. These are direct memory access, serial and parallel. Each type has its own advantages and limitations as briefly outlined in the table below.

Communication Form	Advantages	Limitations
DMA	High speed	Processors must be in proximity; must have DMA capabilities on the processor.
SERIAL	Little interconnection hardware required; may be done over phone lines	Slow speed serial interface required.
PARALLEL	Medium speed; simple software	Parallel I/O required; multiline interconnect

213

The DMA method is most often employed by intelligent peripheral devices such as floppy disks where there is, by necessity, a close proximity to the two devices. Control words are set at specified memory locations to indicate the desired process. From that point on, the peripheral device takes over to complete the desired data transfer, independent of the primary process. This allows the system to continue with other functions until the data transfer is complete. By polling various memory locations or possibly by an interrupt scheme, the completion of the process may be signaled to the primary processor.

The serial method of data communications may be used when the two processors are located a long distance from each other. Devices are available on the market which will provide solid communications over a twisted pair of wires at distances upwards of one half mile and have excellent noise immunity. Signals may be sent using UART or ACIA to provide timing and data reduction or a software UART may be developed. Status bits, normally found as part of the UART control, may be used to provide the "handshaking" between the two machines.

The parallel format is a reasonable method to employ if the processors are in relatively close proximity. The software to generate the handshaking and interface is relatively simple and yet with only slight modification may also be used with the UART for the serial format. For these reasons, it will be the method considered in this experiment.

The hardware interconnection diagram is shown in figure 1. The simplestic approach to this method requires that the output port of the first computer be connected to the input port of the second and vice versa. If handshake or status lines are available on the I/O ports, they may be used to establish the initial contact and to provide data ready or data valid signals as required.

The two flowcharts in figures 2 and 3 show a procedure for the transfer of data from computer number 1, called the sender, to computer number 2, called the receiver. The procedure outlines the transfer of four data words stored in memory locations 100 to 103 from computer 1 to the corresponding memory locations in computer 2. The first portion of the flowcharts is used to establish a handshake between the two machines. An initialization word is used to insure that both machines are in direct communication.

The initialization word may be of any form, but probably should not be something that could accidentally occur such as all ones or all zeros. In this case, a word such as $125_8 = 55_H$ could be used. This alternating 1-0 pattern may be modified to include a multiple word identification such as may be required in networks involving more than two processors. Due to the fact that both devices are intelligent, any amount of encoding and decoding may be incorporated. Elaborate error checking procedures are not out of the question.

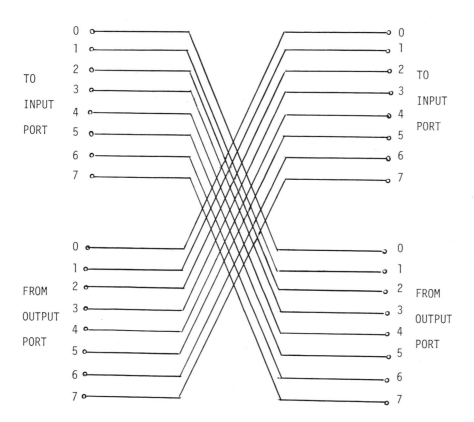

COMPUTER #1   COMPUTER #2

TO INPUT PORT

FROM OUTPUT PORT

Figure 1: Computer Interconnection Diagram

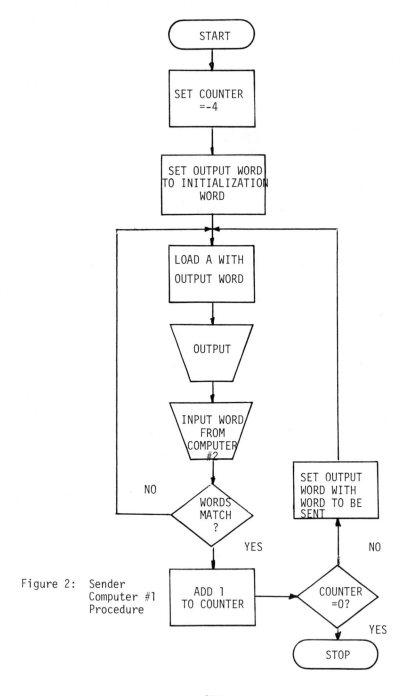

Figure 2: Sender Computer #1 Procedure

216

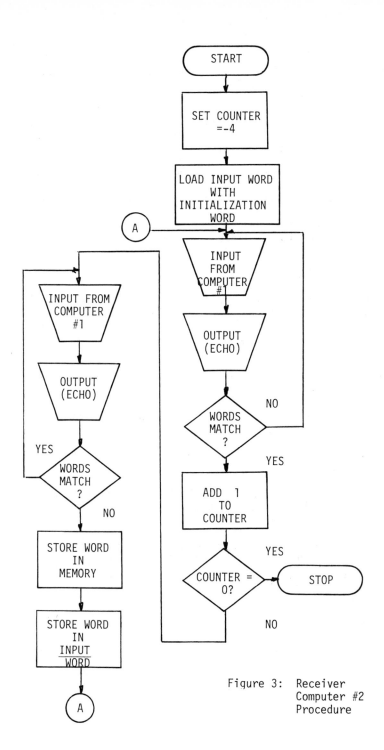

Figure 3:   Receiver
Computer #2
Procedure

217

Prelaboratory Investigation

1. Code the program shown in figures 2 and 3 using an appropriate initialization word.

2. Modify the procedure so that any entire program, of some predesig- nated length, may be transferred from one system to another. It may be a good idea to locate this program at some point in memory other than the usual location for user programs.

3. Can the two programs used for the sender and receiver computers be made to be identical? What changes would be necessary so that the same program may be loaded into either the sender or receiver?

4. How may the interrupt facility be employed so that the system may be freed to perform other tasks?

Laboratory Investigation

1. Verify the correct operation of one of the data transfer programs written in steps 1, 2, 3 or 4 of the prelaboratory investigation.

2. Operate the programs making several data transfers to insure proper operation.

3. What initialization word was used? Are there any cases where this word could produce a false handshake?

4. Further investigate using I/O status lines to perform the handshaking function.

Questions for Further Study

1. Devise a self-correcting error detection scheme to insure that the transfer of data will occur as desired. Procedures involving parity bits and parity words may be employed.

2. Modify the parallel format procedure previously discussed to communicate to another computer using a UART, USART or ACIA.

3. Repeat step 2 above except use software to accomplish the same function as the UART, USART or ACIA.

Experiment 38

BCD TO MORSE CODE CONVERSION

Purpose

The purpose of this experiment is to investigate a serial to parallel and parallel to serial data conversion. The BCD to Morse code conversion will be studied first and secondly, a method for the reception of Morse code will be studied.

Background Investigation

Morse code transmission is a serial form of communications in which two states are used to convey the information. Similar to an ASCII code, each group of dots and dashes describes an individual character. The procedure for the transmission does differ from the normal serial binary transmission in the following ways:

1. Characters are composed of a varying number of dots and dashes.

2. A total of five states are used:

   a) a dot,

   b) a dash,

   c) an element space,

   d) a character space,

   e) a word space.

A Morse code character consists of a series of dots and/or dashes separated by element spaces. Each transmitted character is separated by a character space and obviously, each word is separated by a word space. The Morse code for some of the alphabet and numbers is given below:

```
A   .-          M   --        1  .----    6  -....
B   -...        N   -.        2  ..---    7  --...
C   -.-.        .             3  ...--    8  ---..
.               .             4  ....-    9  ----.
.'              .             5  .....    0  -----
.               Z   --..
```

To somewhat lessen the burden of coding all of the information, in this experiment only the numbers will be used. This considerably simplifies the process because each character is composed of the same number of dots and dashes.

The timing for these characters may be based on some arbitrary Δt interval and follow the general pattern listed below:

ON State	OFF State
Δt = dot	Δt = element space
$3\Delta t$ = dash	$3\Delta t$ = character space
	$7\Delta t$ = word space

The exact value for Δt varies with the transmission speed and the operator, however, it may be said that typical Δt intervals range from .2 to .01 seconds for speeds of five to 30 words per minute.

A typical transmission of the word CAT is shown in figure 1. Note that the transmission interval is a function of the predefined Δt value. The only requirement to change the speed is to change this interval.

In order to send a group of numbers from the microcomputer, a method of storing the dot-dash sequence must be developed. Different table storage procedures could be developed, particularly if the entire alphabet, numbers and special characters (?#!, etc.) would be in use. However, for this experiment only numbers will be used and because each number consists of exactly five dots and dashes, a single word, of the form given below, will be used.

```
        X   X   X   X   X   D   D   D

bit     7   6   5   4   3   2   1   0

        X = 0  for a dot

        X = 1  for a dash

        D =    don't care
```

The table of codes may be stored as a group for easy reference as follows. The dot-dash code for the number 0 could be stored at a base address, the code for 1 could be stored at the base address + 1, etc. Once the correct digit is selected, it becomes a simple process to locate the value by adding the base address.

Figure 2 shows an overall general flowchart for the generation of the Morse code for two BCD numbers stored at a single location. Note that the Δt interval, which selects the sending speed, is an input variable at the beginning of the program.

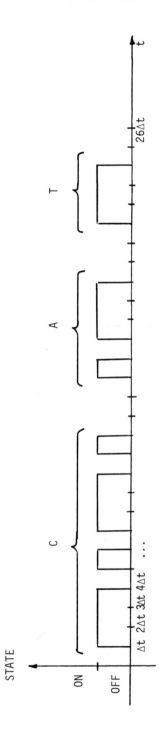

Figure 1: Typical Transmission

221

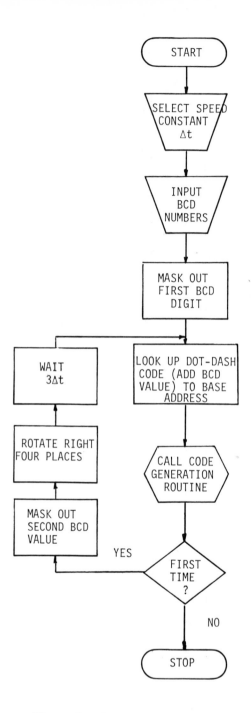

Figure 2:   General Flowchart for Code Generation

Prelaboratory Investigation

1. Draw a flowchart for a subroutine which will generate the Morse code sequence based on the specified dot-dash sequence. (See figure 2.)

2. Code the subroutine into machine/assembly language.

3. Write the complete program of figure 2.

4. Devise a storage scheme to store the dot-dash sequence for the entire alphabet and all numbers. Table lookups could be based on an input ASCII code for each character.

5. Draw a flowchart for the procedure outlined in step 4 above. As an input sequence of numbers is entered in ASCII code from the keyboard, the processor will "send" the message in Morse code at the specified speed.

6. Code the program from the flowchart in step 5.

Laboratory Investigation

1. Test the Morse code subroutine independently of the main program to insure its proper operation.

2. Verify the correct operation of the total system to generate Morse code from two previously stored BCD numbers. (An audio output signal may be useful in conducting this test.)

3. Check the operation of the program from step 6 of the prelaboratory investigation.

Questions for Further Study

1. It is desired to monitor an incoming transmission to determine if the character generated is a number 0-9. If the character generated is, then it should be outputted in BCD format to a seven segment display. If it is not, some other error character may be generated such as F in hexadecimal.

   Using an initial assumption of a medium transmission speed for Δt, write a program to interpret the incoming signal and output the corresponding BCD value. The program should adapt, within limits, to a varying transmission speed and element widths. The measurement of timing widths in conjunction with the input signal may be accomplished with timing loops and interrupts. If a dot is shorter than the projected Δt, reduce the interval. Similarly, if a dash is longer than $3\Delta t$, increase the interval. The amount of decrease/increase in the interval may be determined experimentally and can lead to a program which will adapt to a wide range

223

of sending speeds.

2. Several non-microprocessor based devices are on the market which will receive Morse code transmissions and translate them into an alphanumeric readout. Draw some comparisons between these systems and the microprocessor based units.

Experiment 39

TIMING AND CONTROL
THE ELEVATOR SIMULATION

Purpose

In this experiment the control and safety features of an elevator will be simulated.

Background Investigation

The prime purpose of an elevator is to move people from one floor to another efficiently. To accomplish this task, many factors such as time of day, safety and convenience should be incorporated into any design. Anticipation of large volumes of passengers can be made during the morning hours when people arrive for work and also during the evening as people leave for home.

For the purposes of this experiment it will be assumed that the designed elevator will be located in a nine story office building. The floors are numbered one to nine. A simulation program using timing routines and switches will be used by the system. The system should have the following characteristics:

1. A seven segment display will be used to indicate the current floor. During times of transition from one floor to the next, the display will be blanked.

2. A keyboard with the digits 0-9 will be used to input the floor number desired by the party(s) on the elevator.

3. A second keyboard will be used to input the elevator call. When a number is depressed, the elevator will be alerted to respond to that floor. Up or down indications can also be incorporated by using the 0 key. 0-2 would indicate a call at the second floor and the party wishes to go down. If only the 2 were depressed it would indicate that the party wishes to go up.

4. A indicator (LED) will be used to show that the door is open and passengers may board or depart.

5. A limit switch, simulated by a debounced push button, will be used to indicate an obstruction in the doorway.

6. An emergency stop switch should be simulated by a debounced push button.

7. An AM/PM clock should be used by the program to determine where the rest stops for the car should be:

   a) morning - on the 1st floor,

   b) evening - on the 8th floor,

   c) during the day - at the last stop.

   These three conditions may be simulated by the use of a rotary switch or two slide switches.

   To implement this program it will be necessary to develop a decision tree or priority system for responding to calls. If, for example, the elevator is proceeding upward from the 1st floor to the 5th and a call is received to transport a passenger down from the 4th, the passenger on the 4th floor will have to wait until the first task is completed. Once all calls and requests have been satisfied, the elevator should return to its proper idle position.

Prelaboratory Investigation

1. Before beginning to develop the algorithm for this experiment, it may be a good idea to visit a local store or office building to observe the operation of the elevator. Note the time required for it to move from one floor to another. This will become the basis for the fundamental timing loop. Door open times, emergency stop procedures, etc., should also be observed.

2. Develop a hardware interface diagram for this system showing appropriate I/O connections and identifying port numbers.

3. Flowchart and program various functions for this system taking full advantage of the usefulness of the subroutine and interrupts.

4. Devise a main program for this system to perform the functions outlined in the background investigation.

Laboratory Investigation

1. Assemble and debug the hardware interface.

2. Test the subroutines independently of each other and the main program.

3. Test all routines and hardware to insure operation as outlined in the background investigation.

4. How many calls and commands can be "remembered" by the system?

Questions for Further Study

1. What additional improvement can you recommend?

2. Why should the emergency stop device be normally closed?

3. What additional safety features can be incorporated into this system?

A CALENDAR ROUTINE

Purpose

The calendar is a data base that can be incorporated into many systems and data logging devices. This experiment will deal with the methods used to incorporate day, month, year information into programs.

Background Investigation

Two basic calendars have been used since 45 B.C. The first calendar, put in to use by Julius Caesar, used a base year of 365 days followed by a year of 366 days. The addition of one day every four years is still used today but is not completely accurate. There are actually 365 days, 5.8133 hours in a year and not 365 days, 6 hours. Over long periods of time, this difference can become noticeable.

The second calendar, proposed by Pope Gregory XIII in 1582, corrected the sequence by eliminating 10 days, (the error that had accumulated since 45 B.C.), and requiring that one day be dropped from every year ending in 00 whose number cannot be divided by 400. Therefore, one day would be dropped in the years 1700, 1800 and 1900, i.e., no leap year days. Although this procedure is not 100% accurate, only one day error will occur every 3000 years. Thus the Gregorian calendar remains in use.

Some computer systems still use the Julian data scheme. For example, if the date is May 9, 1980, the pseudo Julian date stored in the system may be of the form 130 (the 130th day of the year). The true Julian date can be converted to the Gregorian date by the following table.

From	To	Days Added to Julian Date
10/5/1582	2/28/1700	10
3/1/1700	2/28/1800	11
3/1/1800	2/28/1900	12
3/1/1900	2/28/2100	13
3/1/2100	2/28/2200	14

Note in this sequence, the year 2000 was skipped because it is evenly divisible by 400.

To develop a procedure for the computer to evaluate the number of days that have occurred between any two dates, a base date must be chosen. Actually, any base date since October 5, 1582 can be used. It is a good idea, however, to use a relatively recent base to prevent the numbers from becoming unmanageable. The base date chosen in this case will be March 1, 1900. Remember, however, any base date may be used.

The formula for this procedure is based on the following:

$$N = \underbrace{[365.25]G}_{\text{Integer Part}} + \underbrace{[30.6]F}_{\text{Integer Part}} + D - N_B$$

N is the number of days that have occurred since the base date. N_B is determined by using the base date and setting N=0. It will remain constant for a given base date.

G = (Y-1) if the month is 1 or 2 and is equal to Y if the month is greater than 2. F = M+13 if the month is equal to 1 or 2 or M+1 if the month is greater than 2.

To evaluate N_B for the base date of 3/1/1900, the following values will be used:

$$G = 1900 = Y$$

$$F = 4 = M + 1$$

$$N_B = (365.25)1900 + (30.6)4 + 1$$

$$= 693,975 + 122 + 1$$

$$N_B = 694,098$$

Only the integer parts of each term are used. Actually, the base year of 1900 reflects the greatest portion of the value of N_B. If only the last two digits of the year were used, the size of N_B could be significantly reduced. In this case, G = 100, F = 4 and D = 1. This results in an N_B of 123.

The final formula becomes

$$N = (365.25)G + (30.6)F + D - 123$$

and will only be valid for dates between 3/1/1900 and 1/1/2000.

If the number of days from 2/28/1972 to 3/1/1972 were to be determined, the formula may be employed as follows:

For 2/28/72

$$G = 71$$

$$F = 15$$

$$D = 28$$

$$N_1 = 25932 + 459 + 28$$

$$= 26419$$

For 3/1/72

$$G = 72$$

$$F = 4$$

$$D = 1$$

$$N_2 = 26298 + 122 + 1$$

$$= 26421$$

The number of days between these two dates is:

$$N_2 - N_1 = 26421 - 26419 = 2$$

Therefore, it must have been leap year.

Using the based day of Thursday, it is also possible to determine the day of the week for any day between 3/1/1900 and 1/1/2000. The following formula applies:

$$\text{Day of the Week} = [\frac{N+4}{7} - \text{Integer Part } (\frac{N+4}{7})]7$$

0 = Sunday, 1 = Monday, etc.

To show how this formula may be used, the day of the week for December 25, 1970 will be used. First, N must be calculated.

For 12/25/70

$$G = 70$$

$$F = 13$$

$$D = 25$$

$$N = 25567 + 397 + 1 - 123$$

$$= 25842$$

$$D.O.W. = [\frac{25842+4}{7} - I.P. \ (\frac{25842+4}{7})]7$$

$$= [3692.286 - 3692]7$$

$$= 2 = Tuesay.$$

Programming these formulas in machine language can be somewhat of a challenge at first glance due to the obvious requirement of a floating point software package. However, a little ingenuity can significantly reduce the problems. For example, a repeated addition routine may be used to form $(365)G$ and a repeated subtraction routine to form $\frac{G}{4}$ resulting in $(365.25)G$. The integer portions of the numbers need only be stored, hence a double precision word is all that is needed. Similar procedures may be developed for the remaining arithmetic operations.

Prelaboratory Investigation

1. Develop an algorithm to find N using a base date of 3/1/1900. The procedure should be entirely flowcharted.

2. Program the algorithm as a subroutine.

3. Develop an algorithm to determine the day of the week.

4. Code the algorithm from step 3 above.

Laboratory Investigation

Using the programs developed in this experiment, determine the answers to the following questions:

1. How many days have you lived?

2. What day of the week was December 7, 1941?

3. What is the first year since 1900 that has the same calendar as 1982?

4. Which new year's day between 1970 and 1978 occurred on a Monday?

5. What day of the week was the Presidential Election in 1980?

6. How many days between 1/1/70 and 1/1/80?

Index